THE MACMILLAN COMPANY
NEW YORK · CHICAGO
DALLAS · ATLANTA · SAN FRANCISCO
LONDON · MANILA

**THE MACMILLAN COMPANY
OF CANADA, LIMITED**
TORONTO

As It Is on
EARTH

➤ ◄

JULES ROMAINS

Translated from the French by
RICHARD HOWARD

NEW YORK
THE MACMILLAN COMPANY
1962
A DIVISION OF THE CROWELL-COLLIER PUBLISHING COMPANY

NOTE

The document that follows must be read and judged on its own terms. Only of its substance may we ask whether it deserves our attention. No external guarantee accompanies it. We can neither specify its origin, which we are unable to determine with any certitude, nor reveal to whom we are indebted for its admittedly unauthorized presence in our hands.

It has the character of a report, not a narrative, for it does not discuss, in chronological order, the stages and episodes of an investigation and the various obstacles encountered and overcome. It confines itself to stating the results. Nor does it permit us to estimate the value of the research methods that have been employed.

For whom was it intended? By whom had it been requested or commissioned? The text contains no formula of address, nor even any incidental phrase that might illuminate us in this regard.

What one presumes to divine from these pages is that their intended recipient—whether an individual or a collectivity—had been already interested in the questions with which it deals, had been more or less informed concerning them, and had manifested a desire to know more about them.

These questions—as the title indicates—are all connected

with the present situation of the Earth, and more particularly with that of Humanity. They therefore concern us quite closely. But one has the feeling that here they are approached from the point of view of an alien curiosity. The introductory paragraphs unavoidably suggest the notion that the Earth is presented from the very first as a distant and not readily discernible object, so that the observer's natural impulse is to move closer to it.

In the second place, the gradual discovery of details seems in every case to be made, or at least to be presented, starting from a point in space that is extremely remote from our globe, and continuing by either a progressive diminution of the distance or an enlargement of the object—which comes down to the same thing.

In other words, it seems unlikely that the intended recipient of this report is among us. It is difficult to conceive of any terrestrial authority, temporal or spiritual, that might need to start from such a distant perspective; or of one which had been so heedless in the past that much of the information provided here could have escaped it. It is also difficult to imagine such an authority employing this detached tone in discussing a world with which it would necessarily have so many ties.

As for what status we may assign the author or authors of the present memorandum—which may be the work of a team or crew—the problem becomes still more delicate. Certainly the text, in its structure, tenor and vocabulary, has the physiognomy of a human production. Everything seems to suggest our ways of associating ideas and words. Everything appears steeped in anthropomorphism, taking into account the rather special attitude adopted by the author: the fact that in speaking of our habitat and of ourselves, it is not to us that he addresses himself.

But the reader should reflect that this impression that he is dealing with a human production is not conclusive. The text that follows is not presented as an "original"; nor even the kind of tracing from an original which a close translation from one language into another of the same type affords.

It is very probably the result of a much freer operation, leaving much more room for arbitrary interpretation, of the type that consists, for instance, in transposing into one of our modern languages an inscription in ideographic characters, or a message in hieroglyphs which a savage of the jungle scratches on the bark of a tree.

In such cases, there is no direct passage from one language to the other, by substitution of *parts of speech* nearly equivalent in surface, volume, content and situation. There is, rather, a resurgence of thought, with all that the intermediary process implies of the accidental, the fortuitous. Ideas which had found an expression in one language return to their source, are swallowed up again, so to speak; and after a trajectory underground seek a new issue, a new expression.

It appears that even between two contemporary earthly languages that are quite remote from each other, like Chinese and French, a translation, strictly speaking, is impracticable. In passing from one language to the other, the translator is obliged to make a detour, sometimes one that is quite winding and adventurous, through the region of thought where ideas and images occupy the foreground, perceiving words only at a distance and signaling to them with a choice involving a great deal of freedom or unexpectedness.

Futhermore such transpositions—by indirect reference and more or less distant resurgence—can give rise to extremely misleading inductions as to the appearance of the original. We want to exclaim: "How much this series, this arrangement of words and ideas, resembles our own! One of us would not have expressed himself differently!" And we immediately suspect that no Chinese original exists, that everything—words and thoughts alike—is a product fabricated among us. We forget that everything has been necessarily rethought and reexpressed for our benefit.

In an analogous manner, the human, all too human aspect of the text that follows does not warrant the assumption that only men—and specifically men from one of our advanced civilizations—could have conceived and written it in its original version. What we must know is whether, when we speak of the "universality of the mind," we mean by universality a microscopic "locality"; and whether, on the other hand, we admit that the mind controls its means of expression and is capable of a limitless ingenuity in their manipulation and substitution.

This memorandum contains, aside from certain significant lacunae whose reason is always clear, a number of errors that are obvious to the most cursory inspection, and more frequent faults of perspective (which are readily conceivable, if one admits an extraterrestrial authorship). One can also reproach the text for certain ill-founded or patently incorrect conjectures. But on the whole, what seems to us most striking is the penetration and exactitude of the assertions. If such exactitude is not always infallible, the penetration is on more than one occasion prodigious, if we grant the hypothesis of an externally conducted investigation. How have extraterrestrial observers been able to acquire such detailed knowledge, particularly since these details concern not only material facts which are not at all obvious, but often, too, moral facts, states of mind? This is one of the strongest arguments for human authorship of the report. In any case, it is evident that information of human origin has been utilized. The text of the report contains, moreover, explicit acknowledgment of such information.

On the other hand, the human reader may be shocked by a certain lack of consistency in the ideas, by the absence of transitions, or by vices of proportion in the development of certain subjects. The material is rather badly put together. More than once the reader has the impression that the author has transcribed his notes without troubling overmuch to cast them into a well balanced and continuous narrative.

Let us remember that our preference for order, in this genre of works, has not been equally imperious in every age; indeed even for human minds it may not be so natural as we are tempted to suppose. Without going back as far as the ancient literatures, whose capital works of philosophy or natural science sin gravely by analogous defects of proportion or coherence, nor even to the Renaissance which did not show itself much more severe in this respect, as late as the eighteenth century we find a Montesquieu, in his *Spirit of the Laws*, treating matters of equal importance sometimes in ten lines and sometimes in ten pages, depending on his whim!

Lastly, let us remark that the "other reports" alluded to in the text that follows have escaped our research. Perhaps they would have afforded us clues to the problem of attribution we have raised.

CONTENTS

As It Is on
EARTH

⇒ I ⇐

GENERAL PHYSICAL CONDITIONS

THE FOLLOWING MEMORANDUM WILL NOT DISCUSS QUESTIONS relating to the Earth's situation in the universe. Nor will it include the study of the physical conditions proper to this planet, since they comprise the object of another report.

Nonetheless it may be found useful to review several essential notions, which no longer seem contestable; in particular, those which serve to explain the presence of living beings on the Earth and the forms which the development of life has taken there.

The earth is situated in the central region of space HZB[1] and occupies virtually the position attributed to it. Measurable differences from the standard estimates are of minor importance and of interest only to specialists.

At distance of approximately twenty-five units[2] affords the best over-all view of the Earth. The planet appears in

[1] We do not know to what space nomenclature this expression belongs.

[2] A remark analogous to the preceding one. The lines which follow nonetheless permit an approximation.

a shifting envelope—opaque in many places, more or less transparent in others, in still others almost torn—whose thickness is less than two units. Approaching from the illuminated side, the planet below seems quite luminous; one has the illusion that this light emanates from the globe and that its ebullition raises and rends the envelope.

This envelope is constituted of a gaseous atmosphere, itself quite transparent, at the bottom of which trail masses of vapors and mists. These form a kind of deposit which shifts constantly, although slowly. Small eddies are observable here and there. The impression of lacerations in the envelope derives from the inequalities of this deposit. Discharges of an electrical nature also occur here. Their rays are readily observable as one draws closer. The series of detonations and cracklings which accompany them is also perceptible. These discharges often provoke, in the dark portions of the envelope, lacerations of another sort than the former, that is, much more local and rapidly repaired.

Consequently the planet's surface is never entirely revealed at once. Sometimes the opaque deposit turns with this surface, as though it adhered to it, causing the same regions to remain either visible or hidden, sometimes the deposit shifts by itself, permitting regions hitherto not visible to appear.

The temperature of the surface of the terrestrial globe remains within extremely narrow limits, and it is most significantly related to the different states of water. As a general rule, the temperature on this surface permits water to remain in the liquid state. We may observe that this indication is of an entirely relative value, where temperature is concerned, since changes in the state of water occur at temperatures varying according to the pressure it supports. In any case, resulting variations in this temperature are slight; for water, under whatever pressure, is one of the substances whose existence as a liquid occurs within the narrowest limits.

Nonetheless one may note that in certain regions of the terrestrial surface, water remains constantly in the solid state, in the form of blocks or powder; that in others, which are more extensive, it retains this state for long periods; but that nowhere does it even remotely approach the boiling point (save in certain cases when it emerges from the depths of the earth). It is therefore to liquid but somewhat cold water that at present, at least, the exterior temperature of the globe generally corresponds.

This predominance of the liquid and somewhat cold state upon the surface does not, of course, prevent the presence of abundant water vapors in the gaseous layer which surrounds the globe. These vapors interfere in many places with the passage of the light proceeding from the central star or sun, and it is they which account for the lacerations with moving contours to which we referred above.

Gravity, on the Earth's surface, is manifested almost exactly as the volume and the density of the planet suggest it would be, and seems to have favored the appearance of organisms of small size, even extremely small considered vertically. As for the weight of the atmosphere itself, it is difficult to estimate what effect it can have had upon the development of life. For certain living beings have perpetuated themselves, and continue to flourish, in environments—for example, the depth of the sea—where the weight of water supported is so much greater than the weight of

the atmosphere on the surface of the land that it is difficult
to imagine how structures essentially analogous could develop
in both cases.

On the other hand, the obstacle which the atmosphere
constitutes for certain radiations and the filtering effect it
produces upon the others certainly play a part, and perhaps
have played a still more decisive one, although of a different order, in remote epochs.

The *seasons* constitute a notable terrestrial phenomenon,
particularly the character they assume. These periodic variations of the climate, owing principally to the inclination of
the planet on its orbit and to the changing position which it
consequently assumes in regard to the sun, have, of course,
nothing exceptional about them in the universe considered
as a whole. What is interesting about them here is that they
are neither violently contrasted nor long (considering the
slight degree of the inclination in question, as well as the
quasi-circular form and the limited dimensions of the orbit).
And since the alternation of days and nights is itself rather
rapid, neither heating nor cooling exceeds the limits compatible with life, save in certain places.

It follows that the seasons, originating in the fashion we
have just described, are in opposition on each side of the
equator; and also that the farther one proceeds from the
latter, the more distinct they are. But other differences in
climate derive from less obvious causes. Thus the two
hemispheres, called northern and southern, although subjected
in alternation to the similar effects of the planet's inclination,
do not reveal a distribution of similar climates. In the
southern hemisphere, the zone where water constantly retains the solid state is more extensive, as is the adjacent zone
where cold weather prevails. It is nonetheless in the southern

hemisphere that the seas occupy much more area, which should temper the climate by diminishing the seasonal contrast. It is tempting to seek the explanation for this apparent anomaly in the slight elongation of the terrestrial orbit, which keeps the earth from being a constant distance from the sun, so that these changes in distance are not combined in the same fashion in both hemispheres with the changes of the planet's inclination as it revolves. Upon examination, this reason is not convincing. The anomaly in question seems to be connected, rather, to the system of the aerial and marine currents, whose formation is affected by not only a simple and general cause like terrestrial rotation, but also by causes that are quite unequally distributed, such as accidents of relief, those under water as well as those on *terra firma*.

The Earth's age and past concern the present memorandum only insofar as it is of interest to situate the origin of life and the stages of its development upon the planet. If one takes as the unit of time the terrestrial *year* (the duration of a single revolution around the central star), it appears that the very first appearance of life dates back some hundreds of millions of *years*, and that it was preceded by a period of at least equal length, during which the surface of the Earth was entirely occupied by mineral substances at varying degrees of condensation and hardness.

❧ II ❦

THE THREE DOMAINS OF LIFE

A SUMMARY VIEW OF THE PLANET IS ENOUGH TO REVEAL that at present life has spread over virtually its entire surface, granting that its domain extends even to those areas where it appears only desultorily.

No doubt an uninformed spectator would be led to suppose that the masses of water—seas or oceans—whose surface is much larger than that of the exposed land, or continents, form vast lacunae in life's dissemination over the terrestrial envelope. In reality, this is only a difference in appearances. If life in the oceans is dissimulated at first glance beneath the perpetual agitation of the waters, it nevertheless penetrates here to depths which it is far from attaining on dry land. Further, it impregnates these depths so intimately and with such continuity that it would be scarcely excessive to regard them as an indistinguishable solution of living substance.

It is important to note in this regard that the continental soil itself is to a great degree constituted, in its upper layers, by the residue of living beings from remote epochs, of which the enormous majority belonged to the marine world. This proves not only that the sea once occupied these regions, but also that, far from marking an interruption in the spread of life, it has been, from the beginning, life's principal mainstay.

Life may be divided into three great domains. The first is the vegetal covering that spreads from one end of the continents to the other. It exhibits vast gaps, and marked differences of coloration and destiny. But the initial impression it conveys is that it represents that most natural and the least coercible form life assumes on the surface of the globe. The gaps apparent in it appear to be accidents occurring during the course of ages, or effects of wear which have reached their term, and not portions of the ground which vegetation has yet to conquer.

The second domain is precisely that solution of living matter of which the oceans consist, at least to a certain depth: it is the most difficult of the three to grasp, but appears on the other hand as the oldest, the one which best escapes the effects of wear, repairs them with the greatest facility and without leaving any traces. One has the sense that if, for whatever reason, life were to become rarer on the terrestrial surface and were finally driven from it altogether, it would still find a refuge and reserve in these marine depths for an indeterminate time.

The third domain is that which designates itself by the name *humanity* and which will form the particular object of the present report.

What is initially striking about the continents, as we have just indicated, is their vegetal covering. But one perceives almost at the same time another formation, of analogous abundance though of an entirely different nature and of a much less continuous texture. It appears, rather, as a kind of network, with more or less wide meshes, flung across the continents.

This network seems to consist of knots or agglomerations, of extremely diverse size, situated at variable distances, and connected to each other by filaments, themselves of several types.

By their dimensions these knots or agglomerations frequently suggest the masses in which the vegetation is condensed and which are designated by the terms *woods* or *forests*. In aspect, on the other hand, they are more like the stony or rocky areas which occasionally interrupt the vegetal covering. Sometimes one remarks in them a much greater regularity; in particular, certain striations, some of which are parallel, others intersecting.

The filaments which join the knots or agglomerations often seem at their inceptions to be merely extensions or excrescences of the same nature as the agglomerations from which they issue. At greater distances, they change in appearance. Occasionally they are reduced to a kind of line traced upon the ground in an indelible fashion. Sometimes they are of a somewhat more complicated structure. In either case what is most notable about them is that they are the locus of many rapid movements: as if their principal function were to allow passage from one agglomeration to the other of mobile elements, whose number, size and speed vary according to the type of filament employed.

One subsequently discovers that these mobile elements are even more numerous within the agglomerations, and that if their rapidity diminishes the agitation they produce is only all the greater.

A closer scrutiny reveals new details and new distinctions. Among the mobile elements, some of which are much smaller and more numerous—at least within the agglomerations—seem to consist almost completely of living substance. In others, the living substance appears to be only a part of the mobile element, even only a small and apparently secondary part, since movement no longer appears to be effected by its own means.

Certain of the filaments—those whose structure is the most complex—present mobile elements of a particular type. The living portion is enclosed in a kind of long sheath. The movement of the sheath is extremely rapid and, for the most part, very even. It occurs along the lines rigorously traced for it on the surface of the ground.

Additional and even swifter exchanges may be observed, which without belonging to the network itself or making use of its filaments, take place between agglomerations ordinarily quite remote from one another. They operate at more or less great distances above the surface of the globe, by means of a composite structure which also encloses the living portion in a rigid, generally metallic envelope, capable of moving without maintaining a support on the ground.

We have hitherto spoken of this network as though it were all one and the same. But it is apparent that possessing the characteristics we have described, it is subject to at least the same limitations and subdivisions as the vegetal covering. In other words, it cannot do otherwise than divide itself into several networks each of which reaches, at most, the dimensions of a continent.

This does not, however, signify that no links have been established among these various networks. A considerable number of the mobile elements which do not require ground support are used to cross the space which separates the networks above the oceans. Others, much more voluminous but less rapid, perform the same function by following trajectories on the surface of the sea which seem to be constant, although their course is not visibly marked (it appears as if they obeyed a submarine magnetization).

Lastly, one must not overlook the fact that externally imperceptible exchanges are effected in great numbers both between the various points of a single network and among the networks most remote from one another. All these modes of connection, which are superadded to the figured filaments, or which occur to a certain extent where the earth's continuity is lacking, no doubt help to reinforce the unity of the entire network.

One question arises here. It concerns the three great domains of life which we have just discussed, but in particular the third.

Are we to consider them merely as the result of a first and cursory view of things, a result destined to lose its consistency upon a closer study? Will integral existences then resolve themselves into the more or less fortuitous juxtaposition or assemblage of a multitude of individual existences?

In none of the three cases can one speak, apparently, of a simple juxtaposition or of a purely fortuitous assemblage. Even the marine solution has a kind of common existence, without which the existence of billions of individuals of every species which compose it would not be conceivable. And it is probable that certain kinds of life occur in the sea only to the degree that it is a quasi-continuous living matter. Nonetheless one perceives here no attempt at communal organization, nor even a somewhat fixed arrangement. Which does not exclude the existence, within this marine solution, of much more limited though more homogenous and mobile formations which move about within it, seem to find their subsistence there, and probably, if one were to study them closely, would manifest the rudiments of organization and personality.[1]

As for the vegetal covering, it too certainly governs the existence of innumerable individuals which analysis would discern within it. But nothing indicates that it is more organized than the marine solution, either in its totality or in the more coherent masses which occur in it and which we have already referred to under the names of *woods* or *forests*.

Matters proceed altogether differently with regard to the network or systems of networks whose external aspect we have described, under the name of *humanity*. It appears difficult to deny certain characteristics in this network, as much in its structure as in its functions. And if we are subsequently led to distinguish within it a multiplicity of beings of comparatively small size that will appear the most active and truly essential agents of the system, we must not lose sight of the fact that we began with a powerful impression of an integral existence.

[1] An obvious allusion to the schools of migratory fish.

THE HUMAN NETWORK

THE KNOTS OR AGGLOMERATIONS WHICH PUNCTUATE THE *human network* are, as we have already noted, of extremely various sizes, the largest attaining several hundred, even several thousand times the dimensions of the smallest. But it is in surface area that they develop most notably. Their vertical dimensions always remain relatively slight.

The striations which intersect them regularly in length and width are the locus of various kinds of mobile elements. They delimit certain fixed and solid structures, in which stone, metal and "wood" (in another sense of the word—that is, the substance taken from the hard part of the vegetal forms) predominate.

The interior of these fixed structures is constantly occupied or traversed by mobile elements, and those which have the smallest volume appear to be made almost entirely of living substance, and produce their movement themselves.

These structures have as a common characteristic an assemblage of cavities, of extremely unequal capacity, which are sometimes separated from one another and sometimes communicate. They also communicate with the exterior; and it is by this means that the mobile elements of which we have just spoken enter and exit.

Each knot or agglomeration in its totality manifests a life of its own which, in some, becomes quite intense. The most striking aspect is the perpetual turbulence of the mobile elements, primarily the smallest ones; the units which they form and which become dissociated more or less quickly; their circulation along the striations, and also along the filaments directed toward the exterior. They certainly play an essential role, as much individually as by their combinations. Particularly since the mobile elements of greater size, whose duality of composition we have already mentioned, appear upon examination to be constituted of a metallic envelope within which is lodged the true animating principle, which is a living being proper or a mass of living beings.

› IV ‹

THE ELEMENT MAN. GENERALITIES

IN ALL THE FORMATIONS WHICH THE HUMAN NETWORK affords, we find, with or without envelope, a living mobile element, which is *man*. It is time for us to form a more precise notion of *man* by means of a closer study.

If we call the network as a whole *humanity*, *man* or the human *person* is the elementary unit at which one arrives when one carries far enough the analysis of this whole and of the forces that function within it.

As a living individual, elementary man is an *animal*, that is, belongs to a huge terrestrial category which possesses, in quite unequal degrees, the faculty of moving about on its own initiative. Moreover, this category, which is far from being an exception in the universe, is discussed, with regard to its modes of appearance on the earth, in another report.

Conforming to a general observation made earlier, and under the apparent effect of the conditions of gravity prevailing on the surface of the globe, the animals do not exceed an extremely modest height. They may gain a somewhat greater horizontal extent, but it is only by constituting groups or agglomerations that they attain a dimension of some importance.

Elementary man is no exception to this rule. In relation to the others, he is an animal of average dimensions, even a trifle superior to the average, if one takes account of the multitude of those called *insects*, and which are thousands of times smaller than man, whereas the largest animals are only three or four times his height, and the most voluminous ten or twenty times his weight. It is true that in regard to distance above the earth, man, unlike most of the other animals, stands on his two lower limbs, which considerably adds to his height.

These two lower limbs, known as *legs*, support the body and serve to move it from place to place; but they are increasingly reserved for movements of short distance, at least in the regions of the network whose development appears most advanced. For traveling over greater distances, movement is effected by that nonliving envelope or support we have alluded to on several occasions, and within which man is lodged, or whose structure he temporarily annexes to his own. This complement, often much more voluminous than man himself, is called a *vehicle*.

Mention should be made here of a curious apparatus which in appearance produces movement but actually borrows all the power it affords from man himself. Its advantage appears to be that the same quantity of power, better utilized, affords a much swifter movement. This machine is called a *bicycle*. We have observed, moreover, that a type of pseudo-bicycle is widespread whose movement originates not in man but in the apparatus itself.

Man possesses another, upper pair of limbs, known as *arms*. They are attached to his body a little below the *head*—which contains the sense organs and assumes the direction of the organism. The arms, much shorter and slenderer than the legs, terminate in two jointed and extremely mobile extremities, which are the *hands.* The role of the hands has always been an extremely important one, for they have served man as an instrument for all his labors, and still remain the indispensable intermediary between him and the artificial instruments and various machines by which he is increasingly surrounded.

The extremities of the lower limbs are called *feet.* Their role, essential in movement, has been for the most part less varied than that of the hands. The word for *foot* has even been appropriated, in certain languages of the earth, for a pejorative use to designate clumsiness and stupidity. This seems unfair, particularly since in the use of certain tools and machines which have recently multiplied the foot has found new and sometimes delicate opportunities to render itself useful.

Man is constituted to live in an atmosphere whose composition has been studied and whose formula is given in another report. He seems capable of tolerating a change in the proportions and particularly in the pressure of this atmosphere up to a certain point.

It is difficult to determine what kind of food is most natural to him. Perhaps he originally absorbed parts of vegetal growths for the most part (particularly *roots* and *fruits,* as the small and agile animals from which he is descended had done). But all considerations seem to indicate that he early turned to hunting animals much more voluminous and closer to himself than the insects, in order to nourish himself upon their flesh. Where he lived near the sea, he grew accustomed in the same way to consume the flesh of marine animals. At present, man has succeeded in introducing into his alimentation substances so numerous and so varied that it is to be wondered how many among them are actually suited to his organism. He also adds to this diversity of substances that of their preparation, in which he exhibits an extreme ingenuity, although the principle common to many of them is the prolonged immersion of the aliment in boiling water accompanied by other ingredients. In other cases, the aliments are subjected to the direct action of fire. It is to be noted, nonetheless, that the increasingly popular custom of consuming some foodstuffs in the raw state is not a return to primitive conditions but, on the contrary, the mark of a certain refinement.

Like most animals and animate beings, men are divided into two large categories, males and females, which are designated by the names *men* and *women* (in many languages of the earth, the same word serves to refer to the *human being* in general and to the *male*). These two categories, or *sexes*, contain a nearly equal number of individuals, a fact which might be surprising, since the existence of the sexes seems to have as its object the reproduction of the type—the male fertilizing the female from whom the new individual issues —and since a single man can easily fertilize a great number of females. But we shall return to questions relating to the sexes in a special chapter.

Another division apparent among men is that of races (or varieties of the human type, each presenting a group of distinctive characteristics though still belonging to the type itself). Certain of these races are difficult to define; their characteristics are of uncertain stability, so that one occasionally wonders whether they do not exist more in words than in fact. Others, on the contrary, offer extremely marked differences; in particular the three known as the *white*, *yellow* and *black races*.

The duration of life, among human individuals, seems to

reach a maximum of one hundred terrestrial years (one hundred such years constitute a *century*). But most of them die long before attaining this age; some at the very beginning of life, when their organs are still delicate and unaccustomed to the difficulties of the environment; others upon maturity, when these same organs betray a precocious exhaustion; still others at any age because of *disease* or *accident*.

Any unexpected encounter of the organism with conditions which do not permit life or which critically disturb it may be considered as an *accident*. For example, when a man falls into the water and sinks beneath its surface, he soon perishes for lack of organs capable of extracting the air dissolved in it which he requires in order to live. This is an accident. Similarly when, during the course of a high-speed movement, he is projected against a solid body of a certain demension.

Accidents can be provoked. They can even take the form of a direct attack with the intention of causing death. One then says that there has been a *murder*.

Disease is an apparently spontaneous disorder, sometimes followed by death. It assumes extremely diverse forms. We shall return to this question in the chapter devoted to *medicine*.

Let us note at this point, however, that the forms of disease which affect man seem much more numerous and varied than those which afflict the other animals; this may be only an effect of the scrupulous attention man accords his own condition; or perhaps his very concern to preserve his life—at least, as a general rule—has augmented the proportion of individuals who are badly constituted and lacking in resistance; or else the gradual extension of the *human network* and the multiplication of the movements that occur within it may facilitate the dissemination of the disease germs we shall discuss below, each part of the network thus becoming capable of communicating to others, even to most of the others, disease germs which would otherwise have remained confined to the one.

All the differences which we have discussed, and those which we could further instance, between man and the other animals are somehow connected to the existence of the *human network*, either because they result from it or because they help to explain it. This network is in itself a unique phenomenon. Other animals live in associations; but the agglomerations which they constitute generally show only the vaguest unity and the most rudimentary structure. Even in cases where this structure assumes a precise and constant character, as among certain animals of extremely small size such as the insects, relations among the agglomerations remain nonexistent or purely fortuitous. And the animal type in question, though found virtually everywhere on the Earth's surface, has never produced anything that even resembles the occupation of this surface by a continuous network.

The exceptional character of the *human network* as of the elements—living or nonliving—which constitute it, a character which has been merely accentuated over the centuries, would be inexplicable without the phenomenon of *language*. Language, or a means of communication by articulated sounds more or less accompanied by gestures, appears to be as old as humanity itself.

» V «

ORIGINS OF PRIMITIVE MAN

IT IS DIFFICULT TO DETERMINE THE PERIOD AT WHICH MAN made his appearance on the Earth. On this point and on those connected with it, we have been able to obtain virtually no information by direct and verified observation. We have had to content ourselves with those notions humanity itself possesses, or supposes it possesses, as to its past; subjecting them, when it was possible to do so, to critical scrutiny. It follows that they include errors which we have not been in a position to exclude in every case.

Man's immediate predecessor was doubtless an animal which already resembled him in many points, but which itself had for more or less remote ancestors certain animals of small size, of agile and restless rather than vigorous nature, to which we have already alluded.

An initial controversy exists concerning this transformation from animal to man. There have in fact been found, on the earth's surface, remains of living beings which can be considered either as primitive men or as intermediary types which herald man without actually realizing him. The question moreover, is of little importance. In any case, the past of humanity consists of not less than several hundreds of thousands of years.

Another dispute derives from the very notable differences which subsist among the human races. These differences are particularly striking among certain of the latter, despite the mixtures that have continually occurred down through the ages, and although each race has been obliged to endure a succession of varied climates, which should, on the whole, have attenuated these differences and favored the establishment of an average type. It is undeniable, for instance, that if one places side by side a representative of the race known as *Pygmies*, which is still to be found in considerable numbers in the center of the continent called *Africa*, and a representative of the race known as *Scandinavian*, which predominates in the north of the continent called *Europe*, it appears difficult to connect them by filiation to the same type of primitive man. It one must attribute a common ancestor to them, one is tempted to seek such a being in the more remote past.

In other words, several types of animals, closely related among themselves and already possessing many of man's characteristics, may have appeared in various places, at more or less distant periods. Subsequently, their representatives may have met and mingled, whence issued mixed types; but these hybrids were neither constant nor general enough to produce everywhere a fusion in which the original types would have become indiscernible. And in fact certain groups, or *tribes*, may have escaped the majority of these possibilities of hybridization, or may have had tens of centuries to reabsorb several extremely partial effects; consequently they would present, even today, virtually the same characteristics of one of the primitive types. (For instance, the African *Pygmies* cited above.)

The principal interest of this discussion resides in the importance that must be attached to the present differences among the races. The very concept of the *human network* and of its future depends on it.

We may now attempt to speculate how this network developed. The point of departure seems to be of necessity located in one of the dense regions of vegetal covering, one of those, probably, which enjoy a warm and humid climate, and already shelter a great variety of animals. A small group of these animals first manifested the characteristics which already made it into a human group, without its being possible to say whether the new characteristics had been introduced by an individual and its progeniture, or whether they had taken undivided possession of this small collectivity from the start.

One may also conjecture that several individuals, without contact with one another, made their appearance at almost the same time in neighboring regions, each possessing these new characteristics under the effect of similar environmental influences. These new characteristics, which distinguished and isolated them from their congeners, or even exposed them to their hostility, might have brought them closer together among themselves and influenced them to unite, thereby forming a new group whose characteristics were initially different in all its members, from those in which the anterior type was being perpetuated.

It must also be admitted that the event, under one aspect or the other, might have occurred in several places, and on several occasions, producing at first only failures which left no traces whatever.

In any case, at least one of these little groups managed to survive and to assure its posterity. This posterity, perhaps conglomerate at the start, sooner or later fragmented. The little groups that emerged from it scattered through the vegetal covering, sustaining combats against the representatives of the old type and against various animals. The life of such groups was not associated with specific sites. They frequented *migration zones* which they abandoned when their prey was exhausted or changed its own territory. They were purely mobile elements.

● VI ●

DEVELOPMENT OF THE
HUMAN NETWORK

MANY THOUSANDS OF YEARS WERE PROBABLY NECESSARY IN order for several of these groups or tribes to acquire the desire to attach themselves to a site; whether this site was a series of rock caves, particularly appropriate for hiding and defense, or a forest clearing in which a hitherto nomadic tribe was tempted to build permanent shelters, using materials taken from the forest itself.

It is from this point that the first meshes of the human network date. The repeated migrations from cave to river bank, or from one group of shelters to another, eventually traced paths. Wide expanses, where only occasional individuals risked traversing a vegetation difficult to penetrate, separated these first elements of the network, and much more enormous ones stretched beyond, virgin of all human infiltration.

The image of this development is not greatly modified, if we admit the independent appearance, at various periods, of several primitive types, related but distinct. Instead of a single point of origin, we have several; similarly, more than one

24

early form of the network. For a long time, each of these risked its being, and reinforced itself as well as it could, in ignorance of the rest. Contacts may have taken centuries to occur; and centuries more may have elapsed before these contacts were more than inconsequential meetings or individual combats in the forest.

Whatever the case, it was in the south of the continent called *Asia* that seems most plausible to locate this or these points of departure; that is, in a region near the equator, enjoying a climate warm and humid even today, and covered with luxuriant vegetation. Several types, or *species*, destined to perpetuate themselves under the name of men, may have appeared here, some hundreds or thousands of years apart. Or else, during a similar space of time, several strongly characterized varieties may have emerged from a species of a single origin.

These related species, or these varieties of the same species, as they increased in number, exerted a certain inhibitory effect upon one another, to which may be added the gradual and reversible effects of the climate and the spontaneous tendency of men to venture in search of new resources. Consequently they were gradually divided, the direction taken by each being due to chance or to natural preferences for cold or heat, attraction to or fear of the sea. For the same reason, each was able to encounter conditions of life which were to consolidate and fortify initial characteristics.

Thus the so-called *white race*—or the race which was ultimately to characterize itself as such—may have headed northwest and then west in order to reach what is now called *Europe*; while the so-called *yellow race* spread north and northeast; and the black race either ventured toward the sea, scattering on small areas of dry land, the *East Indies*, situated to the south, the southeast and the southwest of Asia, then spreading throughout Africa; or else achieved this dispersion without leaving the mainland, traversing land bridges which have subsequently disappeared.

Upon these age-old routes, the races or their extreme forbears could not fail to meet one another and either engage in battle or produce hybrid children. Consequently, in many regions of the earth, we encounter almost insuperable difficulties in discovering precisely which race are mingled there, at what periods and in what proportions.

Lastly, there are cases for which the preceding theory does not provide a very satisfactory explanation. That for instance, of the African *Pygmies*, already referred to above. Simple as it would be to regard them as the descendants of a race, or rather of a species, born in the very heart of Africa, remaining in one place, apart from all mixtures, in the isolation of the forests—descendents who may have degenerated but nonetheless serving most of the characteristics of the primitive type—yet one hesitates to represent them as issuing from a migratory and bold people who, having left southern Asia, might have crossed the oceans, or vast unknown territories, overcoming all kinds of obstacles and managing to avoid innumerable occasions of hybridization before imprisoning themselves in the African forest in order to lead a separate, virtually animal life, and to preserve over tens of centuries so particular a human type.

The difficulty is no longer the same if one adopts a recent theory according to which the origin of humanity is to be situated not in southern Asia but precisely in the heart of Africa. It is true that in this case the difficulty would reappear elsewhere, or in another form; for instance apropos of the indigenous people of the small continent known as *Aus-*

tralia; or of the tribes surviving in scattered groups and more or less analogous to the Pygmies, such as the *Negritos*.

As for the continent called *America*, it requires in its totality a special consideration. Until fairly recent times, its existence was unknown or barely suspected on the other continents. Yet a human network had already subsisted there for some time, though it was far from covering the entire land mass, and though it remained very slack and pitted with lacunae. In all likelihood, it had not originally been formed on this continent. The most widely held opinion is that it resulted from an Asian migration at the period when northern Asia was connected to North America by a land bridge. Some conjecture that another migration occurred in the south, from the islands which are scattered over the ocean in the direction of Asia. The two migrations finally made contact with each other. If we accept the former theory as well, both derived, as to their origin, from the same hot and humid regions of southern Asia. They would therefore have reunited on American soil after a very long separation.

These ancient population shifts were followed by a period when the very notion of America's existence seemed to vanish on the other continents. And it required a new migration, this time from Europe, to rediscover it less than five centuries ago, and begin a new network there which, in many points, has substituted itself for the old one without leaving any traces, but has in particular developed much more intensively, producing much stronger and more numerous agglomerations, much thicker, denser and more robust filaments; in short, with characteristics which have grown increasingly similar to those of the European network and appear in modern times, at least in places, to exceed them in every particular.

Since on the other hand this latest migration, effected by
the white race, soon provoked toward the American continent—more by the effect of constraint, indeed, than by that
of a sponstaneous attraction—an afflux of the black race
which lasted more than two centuries, the American continent has finally formed a common meeting place for the
three chief races; yet not a site of fusion, for in many places
their individual elements, although generally participating in
the same structures, have a tendency to remain distinct.

It is important at this point to allow for a factor which has
always strongly influenced the movement of races, their
distribution and their mixture. This is *war*. One may define
war as an enterprise by which one human collectivity attempts to subjugate another, to seize its wealth, and even, in
certain cases, to destroy it altogether by the use of violent
means of which the chief is the murder of persons. The
origins of war are evidently extremely remote and in one
form or another may be traced back as far as those of
animal life itself. But among animals and primitive men, war,
strictly speaking, does not yet exist, and does not appear until
the network has acquired a certain consistency. Then war is
established as a disease of the network, whose ravages are
initially sporadic and limited. But that it is a morbid development appears virtually incontestable. While in effect the
other relations among the human collectivities, or *societies*,
tend toward the pooling of resources and the increase of
common welfare, war seems to take as its goal mutual destruction and improverishment. Hitherto, this corrosive action,
costly as it may have been, was in part recompensed by the
advantages which it afforded the most industrious and ener-
getic collectivities. This threatens to be the case no longer,
within a very short time, while the negative difference ap-

pears to increase quite rapidly. We shall return to this question, which is of primary importance to the entire planet, when we discuss the probable future of humanity.

Let us note, finally, that for very long periods the human network has remained not only greatly divided but also very slack and of extremely low density. Only in relatively recent centuries has it become dense and close, at the same time that the filaments have been extended, multiplied and connected together. The network, as an integral organism, is a recent thing.[1] Its development, which has greatly accelerated in modern times, has reached the point of posing, with surprising rapidity, another question no less vital than the preceding one concerning the future that is in store for it.

---

[1] Cf. what is said below, at the end of Chapter XIX, concerning certain attempts, themselves quite recent. Are we to regard them as a serious effort, susceptible of future developments, which the human network manifests in order to free itself of the planetary limits? Or an indirect way of increasing the means of interdestruction by utilizing both the new resources of *technology* (this word is defined below) and the prestige of man's oldest dreams?

❧ VII ❧

HUMAN CONGLOMERATIONS.
HOUSES. BUILDINGS

THE INFORMATION WE HAVE JUST ACQUIRED CONCERNING THE living elements which enter into the composition of the human network, and concerning the way in which they have developed since their origin, will permit us to penetrate further into the network itself and to understand its structure better.

Seen from within, the knots or agglomerations that punctuate the network are groups of men attached to the soil in a permanent fashion. This fixation is chiefly assured by *houses*. Houses, in the general sense of the word, are stable formations of nonliving substance, capable of resisting inclemencies of the weather and of furnishing a shelter to the living elements. The materials employed in their construction are *stones* and *metals*, taken out of the ground and more or less elaborated, as well as various kinds of *wood*. This wood, as we have already indicated, derives from vegetable matter —that is, from the enormous category of living beings covering the continental surface without being endowed with mobility; but when wood is utilized as a building material, life has entirely withdrawn from its substance. In numerous regions of the Earth, and particularly in the small agglomerations, houses are made entirely of wood, with small additions of stone, metal and other mineral substances.

Houses, in all cases, are a direct product of men in groups. There does not seem to be an example of a formation of this order deriving its origin from an isolated man (unlike those envelopes also made of nonliving matter— *shells* or *carapaces* —which certain small marine or terrestrial animals secrete). One may even observe a rather constant relation between the degree of development attained by the group, and not only the quantity of agglomerated houses, but also the degree of development of each house taken separately.

Houses are generally arranged in a regular fashion along the striations which we alluded to above and which are called *streets*. It is by means of these streets, as we have also remarked, that the circulation of the mobile elements (which are men) is effected between the various houses and also between the houses of one agglomeration and those of another.

Though the function of houses is in general to serve as a permanent shelter, they lend themselves to extremely diverse employment; and great differences in their structure result from this circumstance.

Their original use, habitation, has remained that of many among them. But in the large agglomerations, habitation, or *housing*, has assumed characteristics it did not formerly possess. Instead of sheltering only the life of a *family*—composed chiefly of a couple and their offspring, to which may be added several persons, related or not, but participating in the common life—the present-day house often forms the envelope for a plurality of families and independent persons.

Other houses, in large number, serve as shelter for *work*,

that is, for operations—frequently complex ones—by which groups of men spend time fashioning objects. (These operations are called *industries*.) Which does not prevent these same men from using as housing the houses which are built for that purpose.

Other houses, but most frequently parts of houses (usually the lower part, the rest consisting of housing), serve for the exhibition and distribution of the objects just mentioned. (These places are called *stores* or *shops*, and the activity which takes place in them is known as *commerce*.)

One category of houses, or of parts of houses—which form, by their aspect, an intermediary between the two preceding types—serve as *offices* and *administrative buildings*. The people who constitute offices and administrations produce no usable object. (On the contrary, they consume an enormous quantity of paper.) Nor do they offer the rest of society, as *commerce* does, a diversity of objects fabricated by the *industries*. But they exercise a function of control and direction over a great number of activities—particularly those of industry and commerce—and also a liaison role between these activities and the whole of society.

Finally, certain houses, or structures, or portions of structures, generally of rather large dimensions, shelter *assemblies*. Among these assemblies, some offer diversion. Others, whose composition is more fixed, provide for the discussion and execution of public affairs. Others have as their object merely to afford solemnity to some circumstance of life. Others, which are held in buildings known as *churches* or *temples*, constitute the principal manifestation of *religions*, which we shall discuss in a later chapter.

Considering human agglomerations, and particularly if one compares them with those one encounters among the animals of all sizes, one is led to wonder how to account for their dimensions. It is clear that they could be much less voluminous, or contain many more individuals in the same volume, if these individuals occupied only the room strictly necessary to keep themselves alive, and even to conduct with each other the exchanges and relations already observed. Among certain insects or certain marine animals, for example, the proximity of individuals in the common habitation increases to the point of contact. Even if one admits that the cleansing of residues from the human agglomerations raises difficulties that are greater than among the insects (particularly greater than among the marine agglomerations constantly laved by sea water), and even if one must also take into account the much greater complexity of activities and relationships, the difference in the space occupied is surprising. It seems evident, in any case, that maximum density in the agglomeration has not been the goal pursued. Perhaps the human groups, having begun their history in the vast solitudes of the forest, have retained a certain nostalgia for it, and conceive everyday life as enveloped in remnants of their primitive freedom that are as large as possible.

Moreover, these remnants have shown a tendency to diminish down through the ages. Many buildings constructed in former days for the use of a small number of persons form a whole system of spacious quarters; and the capacity of the whole represents thousands of times the volume of one individual. Further, they abound in interior details which do not appear to be required in any way by the needs of a collectivity. Even today, in premises that are much less spacious, the ordinary individual surrounds himself with a multitude of objects whose purpose is not immediately apparent. One has the impression that they are intended to create around the occupants a zone of agreeable aspect, a small *private universe* rich in subjects of interest into which the occupants may withdraw when they wish to do so. One may add that these spacious inhabitations of the past, and those of today which more or less suggest them, also have the character of places of assembly. But the gatherings which take place here concern neither the conduct of public affairs nor religion. They appear, rather, to be closer to assemblies devoted to amusement, although they are in general much more restrained, less frequent, their elements less variable, though the chief amusement appears to derive from the mere fact that men find themselves together. They are called *social occasions*.

In a general way, it is unwise to interpret the development of human affairs through the centuries by considering only the ends which the collectivity has been called upon to pursue, or only those which, on the contrary, individuals could propose for themselves and transmit to each other from one generation to the next, like a secret or a heritage. The two orders of factors have not ceased to function and to combine their effects. Moreover, as far as habitation is concerned, and from only the individual's point of view, notable changes have occurred. Until recently those things which individuals, when they could, made it an obligation to gather around their persons were, in particular, signs of magnificence, objects and aspects by virtue of which they afforded themselves the proof, or the illusion, that they were rich and powerful. Comforts counted for much less. A fraction of the ingenuity they expended in elaborating ornaments would have permitted them, in those days, to construct apparatuses capable of preserving them effectively against cold, heat, darkness, and so forth. These latter concerns seem to have acquired importance in their eyes only quite recently.

We have already noted that the enormous buildings reserved for the use of only a few persons have become exceptional, most *families* (the name, as we have said, of the little groups formed by a couple—a male and a female—and their offspring until adulthood, to which may be added on occasion a relative of advanced age) contenting themselves with a small number of compartments, or rooms, whose greatest dimensions are only three or four times the greatest dimension of the human body. One or two of these rooms, rarely three, serve as a shelter for sleeping. Another is devoted to meals; another, smaller, to the preparation of the meals. Quite often there exists an agreeable room where visitors are received and where in particular, those social occasions referred to above occur. Frequently, too, a small area of the premises is allotted for the purpose of body hygiene and cleanliness; but this custom is a relatively recent one, which has developed only in certain countries.

It is among these rooms that the great diversity of objects we have alluded to is distributed. Some of these clearly relate to the intention for which the room was designated, although most may be superfluous. Further, they almost always attempt to please the eyes, thus continuing the function which the splendid residences afforded in earlier ages, which was to maintain around their occupants the illusion of a small private universe. Nonetheless man tends to sacrifice less than formerly to the pleasure of the eyes and more to the comforts of the body.

Although differences among buildings have diminished, extremely important ones still subsist either within a single agglomeration or else, and to a much greater extent, as a result of the comparison between distant regions of the human network. One of the difficulties for the observer is to evaluate the importance which men at either point attach to habitation.

Sometimes they appear to accord it a greater concern than almost all their other needs, sometimes they neglect it altogether.

The agglomerations afford the most varied dimensions (always in surface, for their heights differ much less), ranging from those which include only a few houses to those whose houses are numbered in the tens of thousands. The chief categories, beginning with the lowest, bear the names of: *hamlet*, *village*, *town* or *small town*, *city*, *big city* or *metropolis*.

As the agglomeration becomes larger, its structure develops and grows more complex. The houses themselves, in general, are higher—until in certain exceptional cases they exceed fifty and a hundred times the size they have in a small village. The streets are of several kinds, depending on their width. The vehicles that move along them are becoming increasingly numerous, and assume the most varied forms. Some constitute *public transportation*, that is, serve to transport a plurality of persons not belonging to the same family or house, but desiring to be taken to places roughly located on the same route. In metropolises, some public transportation is effected through underground passageways, and the vehicles, already spacious in themselves, are grouped together in *trains*, as is also the case along certain of the filaments which link the agglomerations together. As a general rule, this increasing complexity of the structure tends to be relegated underground and deploy itself there. Many channelings serve to distribute substances and forms of utilizable energy, such as *water*, a variety of combustible *gas*, *electric current* and so on. Others permit the immediate communication of words or writing over long distances and not merely within one agglomeration, but between two distant agglomerations or two regions of the human network separated by vast continental extents or even by oceans. In these latter cases, as we have already pointed out, the channelings, strictly speaking, are replaced by means of transmission that are less tangible and call subtler forms of energy into play. But whatever the method employed, these *communications* may be regarded as the outgrowth of the primordial phenomenon of *language*.

➧ VIII ⟵

RELATIONS BETWEEN THE SEXES

IN MAN, MALE AND FEMALE HAVE MANY SIMILARITIES IN THEIR interior structure, save as regards the particular organs concerned with reproduction. However, certain more or less slight differences are indicated in all parts of their bodies. As for their exterior aspect, particularly in certain races, it is clearly contrasted, and this contrast is almost always accentuated by the choice of *clothing* (or artificial envelope of the body, made of a flexible and usually thin substance which adheres closely to the body and is not to be confused with the *vehicle*). A rather general principle, and a venerable one, appears to be that the clothing of *men* (in the sense of *males*) distinctly reveals the separation of the lower limbs, while that of the *women* attempts to dissimulate it and thereby transforms the lower half of the body into a compact mass whose base touches the ground or remains at a slight distance from it, revealing only the feet. The reproductive organs are located, it should be remarked, where the lower limbs meet, and it is not impossible that the dominant intention of female, or feminine, clothing was to disguise the region of these organs in order not to stimulate to excess the attempts of the males, who are supposed to take the initiative in sexual relations. Unless the effect desired has been, on the contrary, to maintain the male's interest in these organs by the very attention supposedly paid to their concealment.

Further, in recent epochs, and among those portions of humanity which set an example to the others, feminine clothing has frankly turned in another direction. After having concealed the lower limbs for their entire length—whether with the latter or the former intention—it now seems determined to exhibit them, and to leave only the briefest area to the males' imagination.

The importance which questions relative to sex have assumed among humanity is indeed remarkable, and certain aspects in which they are manifested have much that is surprising about them. In a general manner, sexual relations appear to hold a place in the preoccupations of human beings frankly superior to that which they occupy in the real life of humanity. According to some evidence—that furnished by the *arts*, for instance, particularly *literature* and *music*, which we shall define below—the majority of men's actions are dominated by the desire to possess, and to possess exclusively, this or that woman; just as the principal, almost the unique concern of women is to attract and to capture the lust of men.

Consequently there has been constructed around the primitive sexual instinct—whose force was great but whose function remained limited—an extremely composite and powerful sentiment: *love*. One might be tempted at first glance to see in love one of the best preserved survivals of man's animal nature. This would be an error. Love, as it is defined in the consciousness of present-day man, is a product

of quite recent date, which owes more to the progressive re-
finements of collective life than to the heritage of remote
ancestors.

Indeed one of the facts which most strikes the observer,
and which, by its simplicity, has the appearance of a primitive arrangement which its essential character might have
preserved through the changing influences of the environment, dates from a more recent period than one might suppose: we refer to the distribution by *couples* (man and
woman), so universal today that it might be taken for a
fundamental law of structure. Thus normal habitation seems
to take as a basic element the adult couple, augmented by its
eventual annexes. Many *assemblies* are made up of an accumulation of *couples*. Even passers-by in the street often
proceed by couples. Only a little reflection will indicate that
this arrangement by permanent couples does not have the
character of a necessity which the conservation or the dif-
fusion of the species might dictate. Nothing in principle opposed the male's situation as an uncommitted individual, more
or less migratory, fertilizing the females wherever he might
find them, and employing for this task only the few seconds
it requires. One can easily imagine, given this hypothesis,
groups of the females—or women—occupying a common
habitation which a single and same man would visit from
time to time, often enough to insure the work of fecundation,
even if his visits were infrequent. One of the probable causes
for the failure to adopt this method may have been the
numerical equality of men and women, which is almost constant. The males, most of whom would have become superfluous, at least for this particular function, would be condemned to perpetual combat and mutual destruction; whereas

they could be extremely useful in other circumstances, such as the search of edible prey or the defense of the community.

Further, a theory which is widely held upon the earth is that the number of males, greatly exceeding the necessities of reproduction (and this among many other species besides man) has resulted in the provocation and perpetuation among them of a rivalry for the females likely to improve the offspring; either the female indicates a preference for the best-constituted and best-looking male; or a violent competition decides among the rivals.

Distribution by permanent couples is apparently far from having prevailed in all ages. One encounters it either during the earliest period, in the isolation of the forest and in a form which merely perpetuated the habits of the animal ancestors, or in the course of recent ages. During the interval, other arrangements have predominated. One of the most widespread has been the communal life of a rather numerous group comprising men and women who, far from distributing themselves by couples within the group, were not permitted to unite among themselves and practiced sexual relations only with members of the opposite sex of another group, and this only at prescribed periods.

Another, later arrangement could not have had the same generality, and implied an extreme inequality of condition among the individuals within the same human group. A small minority of privileged males shared a large number of women among themselves, some having monopolized as many as several hundred, which corresponded, at least in theory, to the highest number of fecundations which an individual could vouch for in the course of a year. In fact, this monopolization of women to the advantage of several men took little ac-

count of the interests of the race. But as they drew away
from instinctive life, men had remarked that their sexual
acts, from which the most intense pleasures resulted, could
be repeated very frequently, exclusive of any reproductive
concern and of any seasonal indication afforded by instinct.
Now these pleasures are enjoyed more conveniently, are
renewed more readily, and repeated with a stronger appetite
by the man who can change women as often as he likes and
who, without having to set off in search of them, has a
great diversity at hand.

The disadvantage of this privilege was that it denied many
men of modest condition the regular enjoyment of a woman
who belonged to them, or *wife*. Such men could therefore
perpetuate themselves only in the human groups or societies
which held the quality of men cheap. This custom, the advantage of the few, of the plurality of wives has steadily de-
clined for some centuries, and no longer subsists save among
the most retarded peoples.

Distribution by couples has therefore tended to be established everywhere. One may wonder, given the importance
which sexual pleasure seems to have for men, why they have
not adopted another arrangement which might have borrowed some of the advantages of the system of a plurality of
wives, without involving the same sacrifices for the less fortunate: for example, a system of temporary unions to which
an altogether different mode of habitation would certainly
have been attached, which in its turn would have involved
certain types of houses and agglomerations. In other words,
present-day societies, insofar as the distribution of the sexes
is concerned, might have developed the tendencies we noted
in primitive societies, where sexual relationships, far from

supposing a common life between the two partners, were incompatible with it; in this matter contemporary societies seem to have continued the tradition of a much more primitive humanity, one quite close to the animal condition, where an adult couple and its young frequently pursued its private destiny in the forest.

One of the reasons is doubtless that the *family*, in the restricted sense of the word (which relates it to its animal origins), has appeared to be more favorable to the raising of children. Above all, it accords better with a rather new sentiment, which has continued to develop since the origins of humanity, the affection of the parents for their progeniture, even after the period of earliest childhood. To this may be added the development of another sentiment, to which we referred above: *love*. The great novelty of love is that it is attached to the particularity of individuals whereas the sexual appetite willingly accepts or even seeks out substitutions. Furthermore love, from its origin, appears to call into play invisible attractions, influences of a spiritual order. Even if this were all merely an illusion—which we are not attempting to decide—this illusion has become one of life's benefits which man appreciates most.

Lastly, a prolonged existence in common is capable of multiplying between two beings links of comradeship, affection and mutual appreciation which brief unions would not have the time to form. Since this kind of link has always appeared to play a great part in man's idea of himself and of his condition, it is not surprising that he has gradually accorded his preference to the arrangements which tend to favor them among two beings of opposite sex.

It is also possible that the sentiment of ownership has

⇒ IX ⇐

RELATIONS BETWEEN THE SEXES
(CONCLUSION)

Distribution by couples affords more rigor and stability
with regard to habitation and day-to-day existence than with
regard to sexual relations themselves. Although the fact is
extremely difficult for an external observer to grasp, it appears that the rigor of this binary system suffers many exceptions and attenuations.

First of all, there is *celibacy*. By celibacy we mean the
phenomenon, in the case of an adult man or woman, of living
and leading one's daily life without the permanent company
of an individual of the opposite sex with whom one is pre-
sumed to maintain sexual and physical relations. In practice
this definition is susceptible to all kinds of modifications.
First, of course, there are those irregular couples which differ
from the others only in that they have not required or received the official consecration called *marriage*. Next, one
encounters temporary irregular couples. Those who constitute them may actually be celibates for certain periods; but
it happens that they cohabit for several months, or even several years, and may repeat this arrangement several times

over, with new partners each time. It is a delicate matter to
speculate concerning the sexual activity of celibates, strictly
speaking. A certain number, women for the most part, appear to have none, particularly when they have passed the
prime of life. Most celibates indulge in sexual relations with
either another celibate person or a married person of the opposite sex. Examples of the latter case are called *adultery*.
Adultery is an extremely widespread phenomenon, and admits of various forms. It often assumes the character of an
avowed custom, openly pursued to a point where the observer is justified in regarding it as a normal corrective in the
distribution by couples.

We may note, in fact, that this usage, if it permits many
celibates to indulge in sexual activity, is of wider application.
It is often practiced among persons who are already members
of a permanent couple. And it is not rare that all the interested parties have given their consent to this arrangement,
without even causing the sexual relations within the permanent couple to be interrupted.

When one of the members of the adulterous couple is not
married and occupies living quarters for a single person, the
meetings often occur in these quarters. On other occasions
they take place on the premises of temporary habitations also
utilized by travelers, although public regulations provide no
sanction in this regard and are sometimes even opposed to
facilities of this kind.

Another breach in the stability of couples is *prostitution*,
which became almost inevitable in societies where a great
number of women were monopolized by a small number of
men. It was essential that at least a certain number of women
who remained available be excepted from distribution by
couples, so that each of them could satisfy the sexual needs

of several men. Among the various possible arrangements, households consisting of one woman and several men have been established among only a few tribes, and even there were not intended to compensate for the monopolization of the women by the privileged few, the two customs having rarely had occasion to coexist.

Prostitution proper, on the other hand, has been known almost everywhere and in all periods. It is well defined by the term *public women*, by which those who practice it are designated in several languages. The public woman consents to sexual relations with any man who asks her to do so; she receives for this a remuneration. And since this occupation takes up the better part of her time, she is excused from most of the obligations incumbent upon the other women. Sexual activity thereby becomes an exclusive profession for the prostitute; at least the first phases of this activity, for prostitution, far from being involved with reproduction of the species, tends on the contrary to be diverted from it.

The success of prostitution proves, moreover, that it corresponds to more general needs than those which derive, in certain societies, from the monopolization of woman by the privileged few. Like adultery, it can be regarded as a corrective and also as a complement to distribution by couples. Men who have not yet married or who for some reason remain celibates appear to be the natural clients for public women.

A summary analogy suggests that celibate women, who are numerous, would furnish the same clientele to masculine prostitution. Yet if this prostitution exists at all, it is rarely utilized by women, virtually never by young women. One can discern various reasons for this. First of all, it appears that a woman's sexual desires, if they should be as intense as a man's, are less frequently as imperious and therefore more accommodating. Further, a tradition as old as animality itself attributes initiative in sexual matters to the male, to the point of making it almost a duty for him. The result is that an unmarried woman, on condition that she be neither too repulsive nor too old, has no difficulty finding some man to satisfy whatever sexual desires of any intensity she may experience without demanding a remuneration. Nonetheless, a small number of wealthy and elderly women resort to the services of certain young men whom they remunerate and who by this fact acquire the characteristics of professional prostitutes.

It is no less true that masculine prostitution is attached, for the greater part, to the phenomenon of *homosexuality*, which remains to be described. An individual is said to be *homosexual* when he seeks out and practices amorous relations— emotional as well as physical—with a person of his own sex. This tendency may appear surprising at first glance. The sexual instinct is extremely strong in the human being and save in cases of characterized anomaly, would appear immune from any error as to its object. One conceives how man, in his feeding habits, might abandon himself to all kinds of digressions and even singularities, since the essential purpose, which is to nourish the organism, is always more or less pursued. Homosexuality, on the contrary, presents an instinct which is detached from its goal (the reproduction of the species) and which becomes indifferent to it without, however, weakening in the least. But we have observed above that even in normal relations between the sexes, the concern for reproduction is often permitted to be forgotten. It seems, in other words, that the sexual instinct, despite its vigor in principle, is one whose direction is susceptible to the greatest degree of uncertainty.

The proportion of homosexuals in any society is difficult to determine. One must first set apart those who are homosexual only by accident, either because circumstance impels them to be so or because they obey environmental influences. For example, communities of men living together have always been regarded as favoring such practices—whether these are the houses in which young men are lodged and educated, or else those establishments known as camps, barracks, and so forth, which serve for the habitation and training of *soldiers*—that is, young men intended to wage war. The same is true, all proportions observed, for female communities. We may remark that homosexuality, without being rare among women, seems less frequent than among men, and generally provokes less notice.

It is, moreover, extremely difficult to distinguish what, in homosexuality, is a spontaneous instinctual deviation, and consequently the product of an individual nature, and what merely corresponds to the tastes of a period and its notions of elegance. Down through the ages, we find examples of societies where homosexuals conceal themselves like criminals or monsters, and others where they parade themselves before the public as if they formed an elite. The present epoch showers them with approval, and far from persecuting them, accords them particular honors. The result is that they have multiplied, and to those who are homosexual by nature are added all those who are homosexual by imitation, or out of interest. This docility to the tastes of a period is observed all the more readily in that many homosexuals do not renounce practicing normal sexual relations. It is to the latter that the term *sexual polyvalents* is applied.

The success of exclusive homosexuals has not, however, advanced to the permanent distribution of couples in habitation and daily life. Some among them form households, of course. But the existence of these latter does not assume a truly official or public character. On the other hand, most homosexuals seem to accommodate themselves more easily than other men to a lack of exclusivity in amorous relations. This also explains why masculine prostitution, to which we alluded above, finds abundant clients among men, and also why it comprises many more intermediary degrees between the remunerative profession and mere facility of behavior.

Homosexuality is not the only deviation that affects the sexual instinct. A great number of singular practices have developed of their own accord. Their common characteristic is that they occupy a great part of the preoccupations of each individual and in the measures he takes for the arrangement of his everyday life; but on the other hand, they are regarded by society almost as if they did not exist. It is rather difficult to explain this considerable difference between real and apparent importance. It is not to be found in other realms.

⇒ X ⇐

MEDICINE

WE HAVE REFERRED, IN AN EARLIER CHAPTER, TO THE DURA-
tion of life among men and to the phenomenon of *disease* in
general.

It appears that since the earliest times, man has attached
great importance to the cure of disease in all its forms, and
to the practices likely to defer the date of his death. This
preoccupation is too natural to be surprising. But it has given
rise to curious habits.

We may call in general *remedies* those means—which are
sometimes processes, sometimes substances—by which man
convinces himself that he has achieved the ends in question;
and *physicians* those men who have specially devoted themselves to the study and the application of such remedies. If
one considers the list of these remedies as it still appeared less
than a century ago, one cannot fail to be struck by two observations: first, they are immense in number, although the
majority apply to the same diseases or to the most widespread
infirmities; secondly, the great bulk of them are of an evident
absurdity. They have never had the least occasion to produce any effect whatever, either upon the disease they were

51

intended to combat or upon anything at all, except an acci-
dentally deleterious effect upon a part of the organism not
intended for treatment. They appear to have been selected
by chance, by the propensities of a wild imagination, or even
by the need of finding something new at any cost, when it
was not as the expedient of some imposture.

Now the use of many of these remedies is frequently of
long standing and occasionally dates back very far indeed.
Their inanity would have had ample opportunity to appear to
generations of physicians and patients. In the same period
men had given proof of penetrating discernment in other
realms. Such a discrepancy cannot be explained by the fact
that other studies, or *sciences*—that of numbers or that of the
stars, for example—had been carried out by scientists of great
merit confined to their special researches, while the physician's profession, or *medicine,* had been abandoned to ig-
norant men gambling on public credulity. Several physicians
of the past appear to have been eminent intellects. Yet the
tradition they constituted, and which was perpetuated by
instruction, was scarcely less ridiculous than the popular tradition. One must assume that men lose all perspicacity when
their health or the prolongation of their lives is at stake. One
may add that whereas the majority of the *sciences* afford
only slight advantages to those who cultivate them, medicine
can become an extremely profitable profession. And this in
all periods. It has therefore been capable of attracting to it
men whose taste for the love of truth and other men's welfare was not their principal concern.

Their presence in great numbers within the profession
could only exercise an unfortunate contagious effect upon
even excellent minds, and at least deter them from prosecut-
ing imposture too openly.

In short, until a recent period, everything suggested that no science of disease and its treatment existed. But putting matters at their best, not one patient more was cured, not one less died, than if they had merely been left to rest, and the disease abandoned to its natural course. It is even likely that among this multitude of drugs and preposterous recipes a certain number were not at all harmless.

The situation began to change less than a century ago. This change is ordinarily attributed to the development of the spirit of observation, which has long prevailed, it is true, in other sciences. Why had it not been introduced earlier into medicine? One may assert that the field of its studies —which is the human body and life in general—offers greater complications than any other, and inexhaustible irregularities which deterred the inquirer. This is no reason why the serious observations which were possible long before and of which more than one has since been made, have not triumphed over the divagations and thereby eliminated them. Medicine might have become a hesitant and backward science, but not a collection of ravings.

We shall have occasion to speak of the place which *religion* has held in the history of man. Religion, and certain practices attached to it, such as *magic*, have long exercised a tutelage over all the sciences, to the point of absorbing them. But gradually the other sciences have been emancipated. They conceived and imposed the notion of a natural course of things which it was advantageous to know more thoroughly—even if it had to be admitted that this natural course could be troubled by interventions of a religious or magical nature. But where life was concerned, and particularly the life of the human body, one could no longer afford to regard it as primarily the locus of immaterial principles and occult forces, over which ordinary observation had no authority.

Even today, medicine retains something of its earlier condition. It continues to be divided up into doctrines which sometimes reach the point of frankly opposing each other. These divergent tendencies take the name of *schools*, and consequently relate medicine to other activities of which we shall speak below, and which by their very essence do not lend themselves to the establishment of universally recognized principles and methods, such as the *arts* and *philosophy*.

Further, medicine remains much more sensitive than the other sciences to an element of instability attached to the capricious movements of collective life which we may call *fashion*. The common characteristic of the changes provoked by fashion, in any realm, is that they only somewhat obey the necessities proper to the subject in which they are practiced. They sometimes correspond to external and essentially transitory influences, sometimes—and more often—to the desire to surprise men and attract them by novelty. We are dealing here with a fact already indicated in another regard. Medicine is in a much narrower state of independence than the other sciences with regard to society and public morale. It is obliged to maintain and renew the confidence it is accorded. The notion of *clientele* (which we have already encountered apropos of prostitution) has no meaning for the scholar who studies numbers, or the stars, but has a great deal of meaning for the physician. *Clientele* is in fact the quantity of people among the regular public who address themselves to an individual, or to a group or team of individuals, rather than to others, in order to obtain from them a service in return for a remuneration. The freedom of choice which the clientele possesses inclines the professional to seek the means to attract it at his rivals' expense. The quality of the services rendered enters into the number of these means; but the attraction of novelty is also one, as well as the series of illusions with which fashion surrounds itself. On this point, medicine now, at the same time that it resembles the arts, offers an analogy in situation with commerce.

» XI «

MEDICINE (CONCLUSION)

CONSEQUENTLY, SINCE IT HAS BEGUN TO DISENGAGE ITSELF from the ancient absurdities, medicine has had occasion to pass through several periods, during each of which one fashion was diffused with extreme rapidity, only to yield almost as abruptly to the next; without the new doctrine's ever succeeding, nonetheless, even for a few years, in obtaining general adherence and still less in defeating the adverse doctrines for good.

These variations of fashion have sometimes affected the explanation of disease, sometimes their remedies, sometimes, by a connection readily conceived, both at once. A great novelty—which has more or less coincided with the advent of a medicine worthy of the name—has been the discovery of *microbes* or *bacteria* (whence the so-called *bacterial theory*). Microbes are living beings of an extreme smallness. The pullulation of certain species in the organism is at the origin of frequently mortal diseases. Great efforts have consequently been made on the one hand to identify them, on the other to combat them.

This discovery has in itself been spared by the caprices

of fashion. And it is furthermore incontestable that, since the application of the methods suitable to them, the diseases known as *infections* (or linked to the presence of a microbe) have in general been greatly reduced. But it is precisely the role of the microbes, and the best means of combating them when they are dangerous, which has given rise to oppositions of theories and to successive vogues.

Some asserted the importance of microbes to the point of regarding them as the primary and sufficient cause of all disease. The essential task of medicine was therefore to recognize in each case the microbe responsible for the symptoms. Others averred that microbes might indeed have their place in the development of disease, but more with regard to consequences than as a cause. They multiplied or became harmful only in a debilitated organism.

For the former group, all-out warfare against the microbe took first place. And its partisans flattered themselves that they possessed a general method which consisted of inducing the organism itself to produce the substances capable of destroying the microbe or of suppressing its harmful effects. This method consisted of introducing into the healthy organism small quantities of microbes which had been previously weakened. The organism thereby accustomed itself to endure their attack and to respond to it by elaboration of the appropriate substances. When the organism seemed unable to achieve this, physicians turned to animals by nature resistant to the disease in question; and since it was supposed that the humors of these animals contained or spontaneously produced the desired substance, a small amount of these humors was taken in order to be injected in the sick man's body—after having stimulated in the animal, according to the requirements of the situation, fabrication of the desired substance by the previous introduction of the germ of the disease.

For the other faction, the microbe counts much less than the state of the organism in which it develops. Either the organism can no longer defend itself, or it reacts in an irregular fashion and itself creates the chief difficulties from which it suffers and of which it occasionally dies. This school asserts that in the presence of extremely different microbes the body manifests identical accidents or deteriorations; that it happens to manifest them as well under the effect of an artificial cause having no relation with the action of the microbes.

This second attitude has consequences that are less well defined than the first regarding the treatment of disease. To it may be attached in principle all means which aim at wakening the organism's own activity—instead of affording it ready-made defenses. But in truth the partisans of the bacterial theory consider themselves offended when they are accused of gambling on the organism's passivity. They claim that on the contrary their form of care is based on the organism's own aptitude to fabricate the substance which disarms or destroys the microbe. What they furnish it, at most, is a postponement which saves it from a brutal attack and permits it to grow accustomed to its condition.

The problem of the degree of activity or passivity which can be attributed to the organism lends itself to an infinite number of disputes; and it is rare that an author pronounces himself categorically in one camp or another. It is not the positions taken on this point that have determined the fluctuations of fashion in medicine. The connection appears only subsequently. The principal outcome of these fluctuations seems to have been the desire to throw new remedies on the market. For since the modern age of medicine has begun, remedies are exhausted very rapidly. There are few which remain in fashion for more than several years. This is doubtless connected with the effects of rivalry, which we discussed above. Yet this rapidity of obsolescence is not entirely imaginary. It is a fact that after having effected brilliant cures for a number of years, certain remedies no longer do so; either their major utility has been to stimulate the organism to defend itself by the effect of surprise, and this effect disappears at the same time as the surprise; or, in combating the microbes, it has soon habituated them to defend themselves and to vanquish the resistance which a new remedy afforded against them. This exhaustion generally affects the most recent remedies. A few extremely old drugs or recipes which, by exception and unlike thousands of others, were found to have a certain effectiveness, have retained it down to the present.

In its search for new remedies, medicine is constantly on the alert and disdains no opportunity. As soon as the sciences of matter make a discovery, however remote it may appear from the world of life, the physicians attempt to utilize it; and so many elements are to be encountered in an organism that they have no difficulty justifying their attempts. It even happens that favorable results may be produced, for some time at least. Thus, at the moment when the applications of *electricity* were multiplying in industry and daily life, medicine decided that electricity must certainly cure a certain number of ills, and experimented with it in order to do so, virtually at random. The same was true, later on, of *X-rays;* then of the new metal called *radium.* (For the definition of these terms, see report no. 3.) No reason of principle suggested that either X-rays or radium might have a beneficial effect on human beings; the contrary, in fact, appears to be the case. They were tried nonetheless, particularly against the dreadful disease called *cancer* (which is a progressive destruction of the organism by the development within it of abnormal elements of the flesh itself). After a half-century of experiments, it is still difficult to formulate a general conclusion on this point. For on one side certain cancers have been effectively cured. But on the other physicians of every country agree that the cancer death rate has never been so high as it is now. One must set aside the use of X-rays not as a cure but in order to situate the internal cause of a disease, thanks to their power of penetrating obstacles impervious to light.

Another fashion (more consonant, it is true, with the medical tradition) was determined by the recent progress of chemistry. This science ceaselessly discovered new substances in nature, or combined those which did not exist in nature. A rather plausible hypothesis was that among these increasingly numerous bodies some could not fail to be deleterious to some microbe. It was nonetheless essential that they not be just as harmful to the organism itself. This double search could only be made hesitantly, without the guidance of any directing idea, given the fact that bodies extremely similar in composition have entirely different properties with regard to living beings. Here again, although the research was hazardous, the first results appeared to be quite favorable. But by the effect of a decrepitude which seems to affect inventions as soon as they concern medicine, each of the most vaunted chemical remedies soon ceased to effect cures, or afforded its services at the cost of disadvantages that surpassed them.

Fortunately the prestige of medicine finds resources in

the very rivalry of the medical schools. When the fashion of chemical remedies seemed compromised, there was no recourse but to turn to another fashion which had developed concurrently: it consisted in extracting from living substance the very elements which maintain it in a state of health. Microbes lost something of their importance here. It was obvious that the organism permitted itself to be all the more readily attacked by them if these substances were lacking in it. Thereupon, for several seasons, men in advanced societies, healthy as well as sick, feasted on what they called *vitamins* or *hormones*.

At the moment when vitamins and hormones threatened to lose their power, or at least their attraction as a novelty, a chance discovery made fashionable a new family of remedies. It was no longer a question of substances borrowed from life, but of living organisms themselves, of an extremely small size and not without some relationship to microbes, whose development they were capable of arresting by affecting them with a kind of stupor. Previously these miniscule living beings pullulated in nature. But they were believed to be confined to the minor tasks of destruction. Of them, too, it is beginning to be said that they afford less effectiveness than initially.

It is difficult to anticipate by what new fashion they will be replaced. What one can foresee with certainty is that they will be replaced in one way or another. For some time now, the exhaustion of remedies has been accelerated by the very activity of the industry that produces them. It needs to throw new ones on the market ceaselessly, either to gain an advantage over the rival formula, or to furnish the public, which previous remedies were beginning to disappoint, with a still effective pretext for confidence and hope. It seems indisputable that any effort to launch a new drug, whatever its value, enjoys an initial period of success, which is even supported by results. The illusion is dissipated only gradually, and generally leaves the remedy industry time to perfect a new one. The principle of each novelty is frequently dictated by chance.

On the other hand, certain orientations of medicine can be anticipated quite accurately. It will become more and more of a public service. At the same time, the supervision regularly exercised over the health of individuals will be developed. Differences between the healthy and the sick will tend to level off, for periodic examination will enable intermediary cases (attenuated disease, or symptoms not yet distinct) to be recognized. These examinations will be made with increasing frequency by machines and will consist of measures leaving less and less room for the personal diagnoses of the physician.

This development will ultimately separate medicine from an art of curing, which is as old as medicine itself and which was even originally identified with medicine, but whose principle is entirely different, since it is based not on acquired knowledge but on an innate gift which the *healer* possesses. Sometimes this gift appears merely as a superior skill: for example, a man without instruction will put back in place, thanks to some pressure of his hands, a part of the body, a limb. Sometimes he seems to have recourse to forces of which scientific medicine takes little account—as if the healer released influences capable of modifying the health of an individual. The belief in this last category of healers is connected to a body of ideas which admits the existence of an invisible order behind the visible order of the world.

In the same fashion, what we may call *medication by sites*

is divided into two categories. There is that which claims to borrow only the material properties possessed by a certain place on the Earth's surface. The patients come here to drink the water that comes from the ground, or to bathe in it; or they receive the salutary effects of the climate. In the second case, medication by sites claims to call on occult powers such as those which we shall discuss in dealing with religion. The sick go to a certain site, which the former presence of a personage, humor or superior to humanity, is supposed to have impregnated with mysterious and lasting influences. The seeking of medication by sites often provokes the movement of entire crowds, which is called a *pilgrimage* when a cure is asked of the mysterious influences. And when the cure occurs—which occasionally happens, though increasingly seldom—it is known as a *miracle*.

➤ XII ◆

RELIGION. RELIGIONS

RELIGION IS A GROUP OF BELIEFS CONCERNING THINGS INAC-
cessible to everyday experience, shared by a certain number
of individuals and imposing various obligations upon them.
These obligations may be words established in a formula
they must speak, gestures they must make, foodstuffs from
which they must abstain, others which they must accept,
ceremonies in which they must participate, and so on.

One caste of men, called *priests*, concerns itself with
celebrating the ceremonies, and often supervises the proper
execution of the precepts of conduct in individuals as well.
To the priests are added, in almost every case, various
categories of women who collaborate in the practice of
religion. But their role is generally secondary.

It is constantly implied that the various religious practices
have as their purpose to please invisible beings and make
the latter favorable to those who execute them. These invisible beings may correspond to the various definitions,
may reside in objects quite close to men and involved with
their life, or on the contrary dominate them from far away,
even belong to a world of a different nature. In that case,
they are called *gods*.

Certain religions do not hesitate to conceive of a unique Being, infinitely superior to all that exists, situated at the center of everything, or rather containing in himself the cause and justification of everything, and who alone deserves to be called *God*.

It is difficult to determine how and at what period the first forms of religion made their appearance. They must be relatively ancient. They do not appear to be found, even in the most rudimentary state, among the animals which are not man. One is even justified in considering that the existence of *religion* and the aptitude of humanity to develop into a *network* are related phenomena, each being an interrelated cause and result of the other.

A second condition seems no less essential: *language*. One does not see by what means, lacking language, men would have communicated to each other the beliefs which are the basis of a given religion.

One surprising fact is that the number of religions is so high, and should have remained so since the origins of humanity. No doubt many primitive religions, which concerned only small tribes, have vanished. But this reduction in number is far from having followed the network's tendency to become unified. More precisely, whereas *science* and *industry* (special activities concerned with the fabrication of various categories of objects) have adopted to an increasing extent the same principles and methods over the planet's entire surface, religion belongs to that category of activities, like language, for example, whose extension from one region of the Earth to another has always been capricious and uncertain.

At the present time, it is probable that more than a thousand of these religions still subsist. And it would be quite futile to attempt to learn on what point they might reach agreement; except this one, perhaps: that behind appearances there exists a world that is more real than the world of appearances, a world with which it is possible and greatly desirable to establish relations.

Among these thousand or so religions, there appear to be several which vastly exceed the others in regard to extension. None has truly penetrated the totality of the network; but some among them have attempted to do so, and thereby manifest their presence, even in a vestigial sense, almost everywhere.

These chief religions have, if not truly common characteristics, at least analogous ones. First of all, they believe either in the existence of *one God* or in that of a supreme divinity of which the other divine entities are merely emanations. Secondly, they profess that this supreme being has in the course of time inspired certain men (almost always of the masculine sex) and dictated revelations or precepts of behavior to them. These men are called *prophets*. It is often asserted that among these prophets are to be encountered veritable divine incarnations.

Another of their common characteristics is that they promise men a life which lasts after their death; either this posterior life finds its place in an invisible world, or it continues on earth under a series of different forms, of unequal dignity. In both cases, religion makes of this future life a system of rewards and punishments, thus affording morality and the civil laws a support which is quite considerable in places where religion is taken seriously by everyone, including the malefactors and criminals from birth.

As for the desire to perpetuate oneself after death, independently of any precise notion of punishment or reward, it seems quite intense and extremely natural in man. One might regard this as a contradiction with the complaints man unceasingly makes concerning the miseries of his terrestrial life. But this contradiction can be explained. The complaints derive from the extremely marked difference between the life of man as it is, with its vicissitudes, and as it might be if only the agreeable portions could be retained. On the other hand, the desire to endure despite everything is one of the elements of man's organic constitution, inseparable from life itself, however condemned to brevity it may be by the particularities of its structure and those of the environment.

Lastly, one feature which is found in virtually all religions, minor or major, is *intolerance* with regard to all the other religions. This intolerance has taken the form—almost without exception—of the wildest fanaticism and fury each time that religion did not find a moderating principle external to itself. It should be added that in many cases intolerance seems to have been the priestly caste's means of assuring its domination over the other elements of society.

Several of the principal religions derive from a common stock, the beliefs and legends of a small group of tribes living some three thousand years ago in the part of Asia which lies between Europe and Africa.

The name *Christianity* given to the largest branch issuing from this common stock suggest that it consists of a single religion. It is true that all men designated as *Christians* make use of the name of a person called Christ, who appeared on earth in the aspect of a man some two thousand years ago, and whom they regard as having been both the envoy and the son of God. (It is from the birth of Christ on earth that the calendar now in use among most peoples, even non-Christians, reckons the years.) But the followers of the

Christ were soon divided, and have continued to divide further in the course of the centuries. Today they form some hundreds of particular religions, of which only some have a high number of adherents. One of these, which is called *Catholicism* (meaning: universal religion), is distinguished from the others by the amplitude and solidity of its organization.

In the past, the various Christian religions have waged struggles of extreme violence against each other, in which they managed to engage the whole of society. Consequently many wars have had religious causes or pretexts. Today this antagonism, without having disappeared, has diminished. The sects have realized that they had a common adversary: the increasing number of men who refuse to belong to any religion at all.

With this reservation, the various Christian religions still have their great masses of adherents among the peoples whom civilization and intellectual culture are most highly developed —that is, on the whole, the peoples of the white race. It is difficult to say whether there exists a direct relationship between the one fact and the other. It is notable, however, that since its origins Christianity has been more disengaged than other beliefs from naïve forms of the imagination and from the inferior aspects of morality, and therefore has been more apt to attract populations already remote from the primitive state. On the other hand, it has developed and grown much more complicated, and it is to the peoples among whom it flourished that it owes the substance of these enrichments. It has been impregnated with their spirit. Having become the religion of the white race, it espoused their intellectual and material fortunes. The approximative coincidence of its

domain with the zones of higher civilization has therefore
nothing surprising about it.

Certain *dogmas*, or beliefs dictated by religion, particularly
in Christianity, have a curious character. Those of *Original
Sin*, for instance, and *Redemption*. It appears that since they
were obliged to recognize the abundant presence of evil
and suffering on earth, men did not believe it proper to
explain it by attributing it to either the will or the impotence
of the supreme being they call God. They preferred to
assign responsibility for it to man himself. Consequently they
have imagined that their earliest ancestors had committeed
an extremely grave and unpardonable fault in God's regard,
whose punishment would be the existence of evil on earth.

The dogma of Redemption is even more singular. God (the
supreme being) had sent his son (Christ) to earth, with the
mission to suffer and die there ignominiously in order to
redeem the fault committed by man at the time of the
Original Sin. On the same occasion, Christ preached the
renovated religion that bears his name.

The consequence of these notions is not easy to grasp.
Since God decided to forgive men for a fault committed in
the past, what prevented him from doing so directly, without requiring the detour of this sacrifice which he inflicts,
after all, upon himself? One has the impression that God
seeks to disarm another authority than his own.

It is likely, moreover, that many curiosities contained in
religions derive from the fact that they are constituted by a
combination of elements from various periods and origins,
among which there has only very lately been any concern to
establish a plausible link. And too late for anybody to feel
entitled to reject or to modify some among them, since

respect for notions transmitted down through the ages is one of the chief forces on which religions are based.

In this regard, one cannot fail to be struck, on the one hand, by the lack of agreement among religions, even the most advanced, and on the other by the state of knowledge to which men have attained. These religions were constituted, in fact, at a period when men quite naïvely conceived a truly inadequate notion of the universe, believing that the Earth was its center and principal element; that all the other stars, beginning with the sun, existed only for the Earth, serving to illuminate it, heat it, to orient men in their journeyings, or to furnish signs as to future events. Even when they have made an effort to adapt themselves to the new knowledge, religions have been unable to rid themselves of this trifling notion of the universe around which they were formed, and by which many of their peculiarities may be explained. Consequently, an epoch in which the Earth is conceived as no more than a tiny grain of substance, swept on among billions of others, would never have posited, it appears, a supreme God of the universe sending his son to death in order to redeem a fault committed long ago on this grain of matter, and by beings even more imperceptible.

Religions at present therefore appear in certain regards as survivals; and one might be astonished at the vigor they still possess. It must nonetheless be noted that many of those who participate in their ceremonies attach only an increasingly vague significance to them; and that many of the very men who consider themselves sincere believers avoid dwelling on the difficulties referred to above. Or else they admit once and for all that religion deals with a world which has no common measure with the world of appearances, is confined to no necessity, and cannot be made to contradict itself or anything exterior to itself.

It would therefore be an error to judge the level of human knowledge by the conceptions of nature and the universe which result from even the most advanced religions. These two products are not contemporary, even within one and the same mind today. It seems, however, that religions continue to have a certain usefulness. Where they disappear, it is to make way for new fanaticisms, whose violence is intense in proportion to their youth.

On the other hand, one of the oldest uses which man has made of his thought is to reflect upon his condition. When he does so with lucidity he almost invariably arrives at pessimistic conclusions. Religions avert pessimism by affording man vague emotions which exalt him to a greater or lesser degree. Even the dark thoughts, the terrors which a religion spreads are more endurable to man than a rational disgust for life. Further, to a certain degree religions deter men from vicious or criminal actions, perhaps not so much because they inspire fear of infallible punishments as because they save men from boredom.

But the chief justification of religions is that they are in agreement with a powerful, intense though ill-formulated sentiment which man has cherished since his origins. This sentiment refers to the true nature of the world around him. Man, while cultivating knowledge of that world and attaining great successes in this regard, has remained convinced, not without reason, that it revealed only one side of things to him. He has the impression that if he were to make the necessary effort, or that if new means were given to him, he would discover that in reality the world is arranged and can be explained in an entirely different fashion. He quite often receives indications of it, by the intermediary of certain individuals who particularly concern themselves with it, or who claim that special gifts put them in contact with scattered points of the true reality. Religions in general furnish no information concerning this reality which man might consider valid as such. But they offer him images, or legendary narratives, which he can interpret as he pleases and which, even if they teach him nothing positive, afford him certain desired emotions and confirm him in his presentiment of an unknown world.

It does not seem, moreover, that religion's proper function has ever been the indubitable or even probable knowledge of what exists in one domain or another of the universe. Ever since the desire for such knowledge has been clearly manifested, it is what is called *science* and *philosophy*, more or less connected to one another, according to the period, which have attempted to satisfy him in this regard.

Before leaving the question of religions, it is important to note the place which *imposture* has always held in the life of men. We have already shown that the past of medicine could not be explained if this element were to be neglected.

Imposture is both a means and a need—a means for those who practice it, a need for those who submit to it. One may define it as an organized and lasting deception, thanks to which a small number of associates or affiliates gain the confidence and favor of the multitude. The authors of an imposture generally deploy a great deal of ingenuity to construct and protect it. But in other cases, they content themselves with the clumsiest machination, and with a kind of appeal which they address to public credulity. Their success would be incomprehensible if it did not correspond to a profound desire on the part of the multitude itself, which wishes to be subjugated and led. It is likely that among the extremely diverse ingredients which have assisted the growth of the human network, imposture has always and everywhere figured, at least vestigially. Consequently it does not seem condemned to flourish only in the shadow of religion and medicine. On the contrary, once these two institutions are compelled to grant it a more limited role, public thirst for imposture, which remains virtually constant, seeks opportunities to satisfy itself elsewhere. For instance, as we shall see later, there have recently developed certain forms of the activity called *art* which would not have been possible in a period when the public need for imposture, sufficiently occupied by other objects, offered no occasion for development. The same is true in the case of certain recent aspects of *political domination*.

➤ XIII ◆

MORALITY

WHAT ONE MAY CALL HUMAN *morality*, THAT IS, THE WAY in which individuals behave toward their kind as well as toward society, and the sentiments that incline them to such behavior, is difficult to observe. First of all because man dissimulates his actions and even more his thoughts, and all the more carefully the further he departs from *recognized morality*. Secondly because this recognized morality poses a problem.

There is reason to believe that there are two, three, even four recognized moralities in one and the same society, even, frequently enough, in one and the same person.

There already exists a serious difference, within the same society, between the rules of behavior imposed by *law* (prescription or body of prescriptions dictated by collective authority) and those which religion or each religion promulgates for its adepts. Law forbids, on the whole, more than it orders. It does not concern itself with thoughts and sentiments. It seeks above all to persuade individuals to accomplish actions that are useful and to abstain from actions

74

that are harmful to society. And since one society is in another, at one and the same period, these acts resemble one another; the morality dictated by laws has many analogies from one country to another.

A religion is concerned with thoughts and sentiments. In certain cases, thoughts appear more serious to it than actions, in particular when they concern the beliefs professed by this religion. In a general manner, religion regards as most important in human behavior those matters that concern religion. It wants men to participate in ceremonies, offer the prayers it has prescribed, deprive themselves of the food it has forbidden, honor and maintain the ministers of the faith. In order to be more certain that men do not fail in these responsibilities, it demands that they believe sincerely in what it teaches. And this demand has been based on harsh punishments in societies where the moral authority of religion was without counterbalance.

Religions differ greatly from one another by the beliefs they teach—whose origin is almost always extremely remote —the precepts dictated by religions are much more at variance with one another than the laws of different societies of a single period. Where religions are found to be partially in agreement among themselves and with the laws of society, it is with regard to a small number of elementary and traditional moral rules.

A third kind of morality is that which appears to be recognized by men themselves, and which is derived in particular from their conversations or from the private judgments they make concerning others. It is far removed from the prescriptions of the law, and in its light obedience to the law frequently appears to be tainted with ridicule, explicable only insofar as the party concerned cannot avoid its dictates. Except in nations where the laws are dictated by a despotic power, there is much that is surprising about such divergence.

Moreover this third kind of morality is no less remote from the rules of behavior dictated by religion, and this even among people whose religious convictions appear more or less sincere. Or at least it seems that the practice of prayers, rites and ceremonies suffices in the eyes of many, particularly women, to excuse other aspects of behavior. The ministers of religion do little to combat this way of seeing things, which is favorable to them.

A last form of morality is that which the men of a society practice in fact, and which is no less necessary to know than the others, for it is according to his habitual traits, or *mores*, that each man can calculate what the behavior of others will be. This fourth morality tends to approach the preceding one among those men called *honest*. It is never entirely identical with it. It is increasingly remote from it as one shifts from honest people to categories of inferior morality, of which the lowest is designated by various names such as: shyster, shark, crook, swindler, scum, trash, hoodlum, gangster, and so forth, though no one of these terms is adopted exclusively.

It would be interesting to know if the categories of morality correspond to natural predispositions in individuals. The elements of the question are difficult to isolate. On the one hand, it is certain that individual morality generally conforms to that which predominates in the zone of society where the individual is born and reared. But this is only a generalization; the case becomes obscure when the individual, after his birth, changes his environment once or a number of times. On the other hand, it is a constant fact that in one and same environment, two individuals, while practicing the same *mores* on the whole, manifest a quite unequal propensity for what one may call *goodness* and *badness*. One is therefore justified in recognizing the existence of two more or less opposed categories connected by intermediary stages: *good men* and *bad*. Most *criminals*, those who commit actions which the law terms *crimes*, belong to the second category.

We may assume that the frequency and nature of crimes depends greatly on the society and the period. It appears that individual man, even if he belongs by nature to the category of the good, possesses considerable reserves of violence and savagery. External circumstances are capable of suddenly bringing them to light—to the point where he appears as having undergone no inner moral transformation since his origins on earth. In other words, for at least the great majority of individuals, morality seems to be a product—and a precarious one—of civilized life, and corresponds to no profound need within the individual.

Which accounts for the extraordinary outbursts of cruelty and savagery with which the most recent wars on earth have been accompanied, and this on the part of the peoples who flattered themselves on the antiquity of their civilization. Far from evidencing an improvement over the *mores* of their savage ancestors, they added to them the most skillful means of sharpening and prolonging the sufferings inflicted on their victims.

Even in these derangements of general morality, the difference between the good and the bad subsists. The bad are distinguished by their promptitude to take advantage of occasions for crime, and by the evident and visible satisfaction they derive from doing so.

The men who particularly concern themselves with the study of questions of *mores* and morality are called *moralists*. They are often to be distinguished by an absence of judgment. They attempt, for example, to demonstrate that the good men have no merit in being so; or even that their goodness conceals the most odious intentions. On the other hand, they affect to recognize certain excellent tendencies among the wicked and the criminal, and accuse society of having perverted them. Contrary to all likelihood, these declarations are favorably received by men who belong to neither the category of the bad nor to that of the criminal.

Another incoherence appears in the application of the rules of morality and the measurement of culpable actions. In the periods called normal, men manifest great sensitivity in this regard, to the point of considering as culpable, and even grave, actions of extremely slight importance, concerning which it is often difficult to discern what evil they have produced. But when, for example, one of those agitated periods occurs, known as *civil war*, *political upheaval*, or *revolution*, horrible actions fully deserving the name of crimes are not only committed in great number but are received with resignation, as if they had become quite natural. This is all the more the case in the periods called *wars*. Toward those who are then declared to be *enemies*, the most criminal actions are permitted and even recommended. No doubt some attempt is made to maintain a difference in treatment between those of the enemy who actually participate in the war and the rest; but since this distinction has become increasingly uncertain in recent wars, the suspension of morality which accompanies them recognizes fewer and fewer limits. We shall speak of war in a later chapter, of the aspects it has recently assumed and of the fears it inspires concerning the survival of the human network.

➤ XIV ◄

LITERATURE

ON EARTH, *books* ARE THE GENERAL FORM IN WHICH WORKS of the mind are perpetuated. At the present time, books are made of a stack of a varying number of sheets of paper bound together, and on which the words of the language are permanently fixed by writing of a particular type. Machines permit the rapid execution of this writing, and its reproduction on the said sheets as many times as is desired. The art of manufacturing great quantities of books containing the same text, without the labor of recommencing the writing each time already dates back several centuries and has subsequently undergone considerable development. Buildings, known as *libraries*, house enormous collections of books on every subject. Analogous but smaller collections are to be found in the houses of private persons. When man uses books to assimilate their contents, he is called a *reader* or is said to *read*.

Books can, in principle, deal with every branch of knowledge, every kind of research and study known to exist. But among them a certain category constitutes what is called *literature*.

In former periods, books were written by hand. Their

structure was different; and the time required to manufacture each of them was much more considerable. In still earlier periods, works were not written down on a substance destined to last; they were transmitted by memory and recitation. This necessity to resort to memory caused them to be composed in a cadenced language, subject to certain strict rules which enabled them to be fixed in the memory more rapidly. Subsequently this particular form of language has persisted; but concurrently with other forms whose cadence is freer. The demarcation between the two methods, as regards their suitable use, has never been very exact, and has varied according to the period.

No too restrictive definition can be given to literature itself. And when one considers the diversity of works included within this category now, and perhaps still more in the past, one is tempted to suppose that it applies to all forms of written thought.

But upon closer scrutiny; one observes that literature proper does not include those works limited to stating in rigorous terms special information or knowledge whose use appears to be dictated by the very nature of this knowledge.

Literature, strictly speaking, has as its principle object to furnish men with a representation of what matters most to them: that is, their daily existence, what happens within themselves, what they imagine, their relations with one another, their condition in the world as a whole, the judgment they make concerning this condition and concerning their destiny. But literature is also, like the other arts, a diversion, the origin of special pleasures, of which the highest is related to that afforded by the beauty of objects, and which is called *aesthetic pleasure*.

The role of the senses is moreover much more reduced

or attenuated in literature than in other arts such as *paint-ing* or *music*. When works of literature are read or recited, they are capable of provoking a pleasure which is not without analogy to that of music. But even in this case it is much less accentuated, less varied in its modes, and of a more arbitrary perception. In all other cases, the various sensations that emanate from a book are obliged to pass first through the reader's power of imagining sounds, objects, ideas. When one speaks of *beauty* in literature, or of the *beauty* of a book, this word is applied to a group of extremely complex and diverse impressions, of which almost none is provided directly by the external object itself.

Actually, the literary work affects almost the entire contents of the mind, in the author as in the reader; which precisely accounts for its unparalleled value as a means of expression for man.

The plurality of languages unfortunately makes it impossible for a work of literature to assume its full value save for men who possess the language in which it has been written. What is called a *translation*, or a crossing from one language to another, generally proposes to safeguard the essential and general qualities of a work, sacrificing the particular ones inseparable from the language employed by the author.

On the other hand, works of literature are less subject to destruction than those of most of the other arts. Further, since they are the only ones that express thoughts directly, they are also those whose meaning can be transmitted with a minimum of arbitrariness. In particular, it is by them that men of one period can be informed as to what men of another have thought and felt; consequently, it is by them that a certain intellectual continuity can be maintained down through the centuries within the human network. All those manifestations of the mind which are not fixed in a book have no chance to be interpreted subsequently with any exactitude save to the degree that books which appeared at the same period help to reconstitute them from within.

So capital a function might lead us to assume that human societies surround literature with exceptional solicitude and are careful to see that it is practiced under the most favorable conditions. This seems to have occurred only rarely. Moreover, experience tends to show that literature does not gain by being the object of too narrow a vigilance on the part of the public powers. Its faculty of expression is fully exercised only insofar as it need not concern itself with what the public powers believe to be useful, dangerous or desirable.

But one of its weak points is the obligation it has assumed, virtually since its beginnings, to win the favor of a large number of persons. This results in certain deliberate limitations of expression which are sometimes as hampering as those decreed by the public powers; and in efforts to attract attention or to renew it by methods the author himself judges contemptible; most often, however, in a mixture of the two in varying proportions.

One must take into account this cause of error, particularly in recent times, when one attempts to know a period, a society, or any category of human beings by the books supposed to furnished its expression. Increasing numbers are primarily concerned with provoking astonishment. After having done so by the discovery of things hitherto little known which they attempt to express for the first time, or by the invention of means of expression of a superior effectiveness, literature resorts with increasing frequency to crude forms of astonishment, and does not hesitate to exploit the reader's disgust or indignation at the books offered to him. One can discern in this base utilization of astonishment the occasion of observations analogous to those made above concerning *imposture*.

Like religion, like medicine, literature too is a profession on the profits of which a certain number of individuals live, or try to live. It is suitable never to lose sight of this consideration. And the riskier such professions become, the more those who practice them are tempted to sacrifice what in conscience they believe to be the best to what seems to them the most profitable.

An art close to literature in certain aspects is the *drama*. In halls known as *theaters*, where up to two thousand or more persons may be assembled, men and women known as *actors* simulate conversations and actions among several people in an imitation of the actual places where these conversations and actions might have occurred. The words they speak have been determined in advance, often with the greatest care. They may afterward be published in a book, and then assume the aspect of a work of literature altogether. Some of these writings, which are called *plays*, are considered to constitute the most eminent works of literature that have ever been produced in any language.

⇒ XV ⇐

THE ARTS

THE *arts* OR *fine arts* HAVE AS THEIR COMMON CHARACTER-istic the fabrication of objects that may have a varying degree of practical utility, but whose chief interest is to provoke the impression of beauty in those who contemplate them. It is in this regard that literature may be considered an art, with the reservations indicated above.

The search for such impressions appears to be an extremely old practice among men. Traces of it are found in what remains of their most primitive establishments. And from the beginning they have given evidence of great skill in this domain. Yet it is difficult to know the exact purpose they were pursuing. Did they initially wish to satisfy a particular need, to which a pleasure was connected? Did the objects they were thus fashioning serve chiefly as accessories in religious ceremonies, or as a means to influence certain mysterious powers of nature?

Some of this basic uncertainty has persisted to our own day. Many people still consider a work of art to be entirely justified only if it is useful, in one fashion or another, whether such utility be practical or moral.

Another uncertainty specifically affects two arts, those designated by the names *painting* and *sculpture*. Is their principle the most exact imitation possible of natural objects? Or, what comes down to the same thing, are the figures they trace to give the illusion that they truly exist? It is not to be doubted that artists of the past who have maintained a great reputation sought to produce this illusion, even without having long reflected upon it, though not dispensing with the pursuit of other goals as well: for instance, to achieve a harmonious composition which beings and spectacles in nature often lack. A perfect imitation required in itself such an abundance of particular skills that it often sufficed for an artist's ambition and for the admiration he was accorded.

But men have recently invented machines and methods as a result of which such perfect imitation can be obtained in an extremely short time, and without any particular skill. The imitation even proceeds further in detail than had ever been possible before. Artists were constrained to perceive that other elements of their art were more precious because they were more difficult to replace by the rapid operation of a machine.

These two arts have furthermore been victims of the degree of perfection which they had achieved. During a long succession of centuries—long in relation to a single human life—each generation of artists, by profiting from the methods devised by their predecessors, perfected some new accomplishment. Such perfection might even have been achieved much more rapidly if catastrophes had not interrupted the movement of civilization and caused it to retrogress. Once such perfection had been achieved, the artists still succeeded for a time in retaining the public's attention by introducing a certain amount of variety into the use of that perfection. Since it included a great number of means, it was possible not to utilize them all at one time. There resulted a diversity of combinations which was only gradually exhausted. Yet it was ultimately exhausted, and the artists found themselves obliged either to repeat the works of their predecessors or to seek novelty by gradually turning away from perfection—that is, by introducing into their combinations increasingly numerous elements which the concern for perfection had either eliminated or condemned during the course of time.

This enterprise, after having been executed with moderation and discernment, was carried to outrageous extremes. Some artists forced themselves to simulate the ignorance of their art. Others, who had nothing to simulate, delighted in displaying the worst ineptitudes, carefully protecting themselves against the vestiges of skill which they risked acquiring in spite of themselves.

The art known as *architecture* is dedicated to the construction of houses and of all categories of buildings. This art has also suffered from the perfection, or from the various types of perfection, it had achieved; but still more from the facilities which have subsequently been afforded it with regard to the materials it employs and the forces at its disposal. It has turned away from slow and scrupulous work to construct in haste enormous edifices whose general form has no further interest and whose detail no longer possesses any richness or variety.

As for *music*, or the art of assembling sounds produced by *instruments* or by voices, it too finds itself embarrassed by the very accomplishments it has achieved, moreover in an ex-

tremely short period of time. The search for novelty incites
it to affect certain trivial singularities, for almost all the important inventions have apparently been made already.

It is to be observed that the future on earth of art in general may inspire a certain anxiety. Indeed it seems to have exhausted in an extremely short period of time (some thousands
of years, at the most, for the oldest arts) the majority of its
possibilities; and many of these have seen the light of day in
the most recent periods. Further, humanity endures as im-
patiently as ever the repetition of what it knows. Continuity
in perfection, or in the search for perfection, does not appear
to be an exciting goal for it. It constantly demands new impressions, which soon cease to exist. The arts are doing the
impossible to perpetuate themselves. But it does not appear
that they can employ certain increasingly special and increasingly preposterous means of attracting attention much
longer.

If one looks more closely, one realizes that certain arts
have sources of renewal. Architecture, for example, can
aspire to serve forms of life or activity which the discoveries
of science and the inventions of industry are bringing into
being, without, however, abandoning the search for beauty
in the structure and ornamentation of edifices. As for painting, it might have perpetuated itself of its own accord had it
continued to reproduce the aspects of life and civilization, as
well as the physiognomy of persons, for the novelty it requires would then have derived from the subjects it treated.
But quasi-automatic methods (classified under the name of
photography) have assumed this function and have per-
formed it with guarantees of exactitude that painting could
not give, and a rapidity of execution that infinitely exceeds
that of the artist.

Literature is in a better situation. It can, as painting might have done had it not been for the invention of photography, find a source of renewal in the fact that the substance it deals with, from one period to the next, never remains the same.

Nonetheless, on the whole, man risks being deprived soon of a good part of what he used to consider his interest in living and the charm of his existence. He will owe this loss to the very rapidity of the progress he has made in his various activities during these last twenty or thirty centuries, and even more to a defect in his nature which condemns him to be unable to enjoy the same thing for long without suffering restlessness and discontent.

XVI

SCIENCE AND PHILOSOPHY

AN UNPREJUDICED OBSERVER IS TEMPTED TO SUPPOSE THAT *science* and *philosophy* are for man related means of knowing the reality that surrounds him and of which he is a part. Since religion professes extremely assured notions as to the origin, constitution and final destiny of all things, one might suppose that its resources would complete those of science and philosophy in directions these latter are prevented from taking. But there are a great number of religions. There is also a diversity of philosophies. Only science, at least within one and the same period, presents a certain unity of outlook.

It therefore appears difficult to associate them and also to delimit their realms. The question would assume another character if they had had their inceptions at the same time and had divided up the work to be done according to some rational plan. Nothing of the kind has been the case. It appears that philosophy, initially commingled with religion, has gradually detached itself from it. The same has been the case, subsequently, for science with regard to philosophy.

Some men do not hesitate to believe that science, with all the progress and the enlargements it is still capable of, is the only form of knowledge that corresponds to the present development of the human mind; that religion or rather religions are merely survivals whose antiquity of origin explains their tenacity; that philosophies themselves are justified only insofar as, taking into account the results of science, they attempt to see how these results can be integrated to give men a probable notion of nature and the universe, and also how to treat correctly the problems that even science declares itself for the moment—and perhaps forever—incapable of elucidating. In short, a philosophy would be a temporary conclusion man would draw from everything he knows or thinks he knows at a given moment.

But this position is far from being admitted by everyone. What one can assert is that human knowledge, whatever truly remarkable discoveries it has effected in an extremely short time, forbids itself in principle everything that is not to be grasped in material experience as it can be effected on earth with the maximum of ingenuity. There consequently remains, also in principle, a vast field of investigation proper to philosophy and religion. It is not certain that they can take advantage of it.

Earlier in this report, when we were particularly concerned with religion, we saw that the curiosity about what *really* exists it not what counts most for religion; or at least that it is not concerned with what really exists save insofar as the condition of man and his destiny is found to be explained and justified by it.

Science was until very recently the object of an admiration, a veneration that was extremely widespread among men. On the one hand, it appeared clear that its many discoveries were, by application to industry, to improve the human condition greatly and rapidly. These precise and immediate expectations actually did away with a great deal of the authority of the promises of religions. It was not absurd to imagine, in a century or two, a humanity delivered of most of its scourges or of the difficulties of existence which still burden it.

On the other hand, men could not fail to be struck by the immense and regular development of scientific knowledge, whereas the other forms of knowledge marked time or wasted their energy in age-old disputes.

But this period of unreserved confidence lasted only a short time. The applications of science have become increasingly dreadful by the limitless means of destruction they are putting at the service of desires that may be blind or malignant. One nowadays hears talk of a partial annihilation of the planet or at least of a definitive sweeping of life from its surface by the effect of a deliberately prepared deflagration, even if, in preparing it, its authors had in view only circumscribed ravages whose burden only those people considered as enemies were to endure. And in any case it is remarkable that after some hundreds of thousands of years, during which its entire ambition was to subsist as best it could in the interstices and unheavals of natural forces, humanity should suddenly have managed to gain possession of nature's secrets, to the point of fearing them less in themselves than for the abuses humanity might be tempted to make of them.

Men have consequently ceased to see in the development of science the assurance of a future earthly happiness. But they are beginning to be disappointed by science in another fashion. They have been accustomed to enjoy in the scientific explanation of things, small or large, what was distinct and exact, the exact representations which it furnished their minds, and the unequivocal simplicity of the latest elements it brought into play. The object of a scientific explanation, even of a mere description, was to be fully conceivable. It was actually from this point that science derived its prestige in the face of religion, where inconceivable notions constantly intervened.

Now, in only the last few years, science on earth has lost this advantage. It has chosen to present as explanations essential obscurities that are quite inconceivable to the human mind. Its excuse is that these fictive notions permit it to calculate and to anticipate. But its error is to let it be supposed that reality behaves in this manner. It has thereby given birth to almost as many insoluble mysteries as religion— which causes many people to assert they no longer know by which of the two reason is the more offended.

This separation of science from reason has not yet produced all its consequences. But they may one day become serious.

Apropos of religion, we have discussed the extraordinary naïveté men have so long evidenced in their representation of the universe. They were convinced that the Earth, of which even the most enterprising of them knew only a portion, was not only the center of all things, but that it constituted the principal mass of all things; the stars were merely ornaments, accessories; as for the sun, it was a source of light and heat arranged for terrestrial use. The gods, or the one god, had no greater concern than to supervise what was happening on Earth, and on occasion to meddle in it themselves. When a man had extended his authority over a fragment of the human network, he frequently permitted himself to be called master of the universe, and was not far from regarding himself as the personage second in importance to the supreme Being. The same absurdity prevailed concerning time. A city was called eternal because it had subsisted for several hundred years, a man immortal because his name was still mentioned after several generations.

Science has cured man of these illusions only gradually and incompletely. What he has ended by knowing or guessing of the true dimensions of the universe and the terrestrial globe's insignificant place within it has only slight influence over his daily thought. In truth, it is the details of science that act upon his way of seeing the world. The total concept has little meaning.

It is here that philosophy might complement or prolong science. And indeed it once did. Unfortunately, philosophy seems to have been put out of countenance by the progress of science, turning in a circle until serious minds grew accustomed to doing without it. In its desire to justify its existence, philosophy has rushed into a series of entirely verbal divagations and has hoped it might acquire something of science's prestige by dissimulating the meaninglessness of its task behind an incomprehensible jargon.

One remarkable characteristic is the persistence down through the ages and even to our own day of the concept of an occult universe, of which neither science nor philosophy takes account. Religion admits it in principle; and indeed certain religions make or claim to make frequent incursions upon it. But on the whole everything suggests that science, philosophy and even religion as it is openly professed and practiced are concerned with a certain universe and ignore any other.

It is difficult to offer any judgment as to the efforts humanity has made in this direction. In one direction they have been countless and continuous. But little progress has been achieved. It is always attempts of the same sort that are made and results of the same dimension that are obtained. The excess of credulity and the excess of incredulity that greet them on either side are equally fatal. No tradition of research, as in science proper, has been established which might permit the improvement of methods and the accumulation of results from one generation to the next.

One may indeed wonder if humanity has not long since taken a path it can keep to safely only by avoiding this occult universe, and even by affecting officially to ignore its existence, although it continues to have circumstantial and chaotic relations with it. It is difficult to imagine the revolution in the data on which human knowledge at present is based, and by which it even controls daily existence, if the exploration of this occult universe were to prevail over the mind's other preoccupations; yet such an upheaval would ultimately correspond to the degree of respective importance of the matters involved.

XVII

INVENTIONS. TECHNOLOGY

HUMANITY APPEARS TO HAVE TRIED IN EVERY AGE TO AMELIO-
rate the material conditions of its existence by applying whatever knowledge it has been able to obtain and by manufacturing the appropriate tools and instruments. But for a
long time these acquisitions have been extremely slow; many
were forgotten or lost during the great upheavals of peoples;
and when civilization resumed its course, it considered itself
fortunate to recover in part the resources of vanished cul-
tures.

But for the last two hundred years, humanity's rapid advances in knowledge have had increasingly numerous and important consequences in the material arrangements of life.
On the one hand, humanity paid a new attention to the
forces which have always existed in nature, but which it had
hitherto neglected, or had utilized only distractedly, without
attaching much importance to them (as, for instance, the
force of expansion of water vapor). On the other, it has realized that the ingenuity it has expended in creating instruments called *machines*, with an intention which was most

often the result of curiosity or amusement, could receive a much more extensive and serious employment.

Machines are kinds of artificial organisms capable of producing certain movements or of performing certain operations which more power, rapidity and precision than a living organism. The day when man conceived the idea of animating these machines by natural forces whose output was considerable, if not unlimited, he was on the track of a profound modification of his material condition. It was gradually realized that machines were capable of accomplishing by themselves increasingly various and complicated tasks, and that man had only to supervise or direct their performance. In this way there was constituted a quantity of artificial beings whose power and effectiveness generally far exceed those of man and those of the animals he had induced to serve him.

It is apparent, however, that man expends more intelligence inventing these machines than prudence in utilizing them. His employment of them often resembles the diversions of children. He does not calculate with an eye to a happiness that would be as regular and complete as possible—instead he seeks excitement, the satisfactions of pride and the temporary illusion of omnipotence.

It is thus that for over half a century man has multiplied the machines that serve to transport him, and has also increased their speed out of all proportion to his real locomotive needs. The most advanced parts of the *network* are remarkable for the perpetual agitation manifest in them. The majority of these movements occur not because they are necessary but because the vehicles which facilitate them afford the temptation to effect them. Such vehicles themselves have be-

come so abundant in many places that they have a tendency
to agglomerate.

Those machines which are constructed to move through
the air at varying distances from the ground are those which
move most rapidly and also those which are the most costly
to manufacture and maintain. The resources of all kinds
which they absorb would have sufficed to introduce a major
improvement and truly useful installations in the whole of
human life; whereas the chief effect of the flying machines appears to be that they afford a certain number of men means of
moving more rapidly over greater distances (if one leaves
aside the terrible utilization made of them for the ravages of
war).

Similarly, other inventions have been developed and consume increasing resources more on account of the amusement they afford than by reason of their true utility. Occasionally, it is true, this amusement assumes the character of
an extension of human nature and its powers, which is so
astonishing that one can readily understand the value man at-
taches to it. For instance, what he calls *radio* permits him,
sitting within his own house, to hear words or music produced a great distance away. An invention whose principle
is similar permits him to see remote scenes and events under
the same conditions. Lastly, it has been for some time already that the image of scenes in motion could be fixed by a
photographic method and subsequently repeated as many
times as desired, retaining the movements, the sounds and the
words that accompany them, and even their colors. The
scenes in question can be arranged into a fiction, somewhat
in the manner of *plays*. To view these moving and speaking
images, men gather in halls analogous to halls of theaters.

The danger of these inventions is the lack of order with which they appear and the chaotic way in which they are developed and utilized. It is clear that each of them, being a new means put at man's disposal, can only be declared beneficial after examination, and remains so only if its use is maintained within certain limits.

Yet each of them develops and overflows as much as it can. Mounting interests are attached to them, and no limit is voluntarily observed.

The future equilibrium of humanity has already been compromised by this situation. And *technology* (or the ensemble of applications of science to industry), after having appeared, for some decades, to work for man's material happiness, already introduces an inextricable complication into his existence, in which happiness would have no opportunity to survive, if a much more serious threat had not been manifested from the same quarter.

Indeed, as we have previously indicated apropos of science, an entire portion of scientifically-inspired technology has turned toward the perfection of means of destruction, which war reserves the right to develop. Such advances have been made in this direction that henceforth the belligerents are in a position to suppress civilization and even life itself over an extended portion of the planet. The motives that inspire nations to war being the same as in the past, and no power being sufficiently strong to impose a pacific control upon the adversaries, the eventuality we have just mentioned enters into the conjectures of all serious minds.

On the other hand, there has occurred, during the period of our observation and, so to speak, before our very eyes, a quite remarkable change in the way the problem is posed.

A certain number of eminent minds envisaged and prophesied, in fact, a utilization of "pacific" purposes of the recent scientific discoveries and technological inventions affecting the liberation of the energy contained in the elements of matter. Production of inexhaustible and eventually cheap energy was anticipated (from which transportation, habitation, great public works, and subsequently all industries would benefit). Now it appears that such pacific utilization would itself involve—and is already beginning to involve—to the extent that it has been set in motion—dreadful dangers (owing to the imperfect elimination of residues harmful to normal functioning, to the gradual poisoning of the entire terrestrial environment by the accumulation of these residues).

So that the problem which is raised for the men who direct or incline the activity of the world becomes still more disquieting. It is not enough for them to work miracles of good will, foresight, and lucidity in order to avoid the Earth's destruction in a catastrophe of explosive nature. The danger of the "pacific utilizations," if it is less concentrated and therefore less spectacular as a threat, would be scarcely less effective in the long run. But it is still more difficult to combat because of its multiform and dispersed character—and particularly because of the deceptive aspect by which it is masked.

It is too soon to judge the success of the quite recent attempts made to project a certain distance from the Earth what men call *artificial satellites*. Several of these small objects have managed to circulate for quite a long time around the planet, near the confines of the terrestrial atmosphere, obeying the general laws that control the movement of the planets themselves and their satellites. Further, it is possible to lodge apparatus within them capable of registering useful observations hampered only by the presence of the atmosphere on the globe's surface. But the success of these attempts has encouraged the expression of unreasonable hopes. In particular, one can only deplore the fact that behind the scientific preoccupations thus publicized, these new successes of technology aim first of all at increasing the range and effectiveness of new means of mutual destruction.

POLITICAL POWERS

IN EACH OF THE SOCIETIES THAT CONSTITUTE THE HUMAN NET-work and which, although connected together, lead an independent existence, certain men and certain more or less permanent groups have as a function to control the movement of society, to prevent the disturbances which might occur there, to inspire and enforce respect for what we defined above as *public morality*.

In other words, every society possesses a *government;* and this government, in order to be obeyed, has at its disposal a force which is called the *police*.

Save for exceptions which are becoming increasingly rare, a government does not function entirely as it pleases. It is subject to certain permanent rules, and is further controlled by *assemblies* or *councils*, whose members are most frequently not chosen by the government itself. They are supposed in many cases to emanate from society as a whole, by a means which is called an *election*. A great quantity of *citizens*, if not all, designate those among them who will represent them in these assemblies.

The result is what one may call the political arrangement

of a society. But there subsists as well a spontaneous arrangement, which results from various activities of which we have described the principal ones. One might suppose that this spontaneous arrangement is capable of being self-sufficient. In reality, it never succeeds in being so. These activities each comprise a power of development that sees no internal reason to arrest itself. They naturally tend to encroach upon one another, and their conflicts would be resolved only by violence, if a higher authority did not induce them to compromise.

Further, there is always in a society a certain proportion of individuals who are malefactors almost from birth. Their presence is tolerable only to the degree that they are intimidated by public force. They alone would render impractical the spontaneous arrangement of societies. There could not even be a question, in such a case, of excluding or destroying them beforehand. For these two operations would require the employment of a concerted force which could only be of a public nature and which would tend to maintain itself lastingly. Moreover these operations would have to be recommenced each time a criminal, having remained virtually invisible hitherto, would manifest himself by his actions.

One of the important aspects of the social arrangement is the way in which wealth is produced and distributed. It is remarkable that up to a recent period the distribution of wealth has been prodigiously unequal. Hence an extreme *inequality of condition* among men.

The origin of this inequality can no doubt be found in the periods when a first organization of society had been effected by violence and where the differences in condition corresponded in general to the differences between the powers each man possessed to impose his will or make it respected.

But these periods are now remote; their influence could have vanished.

It appears that new forms of power, and other sources of inequality have subsequently replaced violence proper and its effects. One of these forms of power is the accumulation of *money* and of the means of obtaining it. Since money serves to remunerate labor, whoever possesses a great deal of money can put at his service the labor of a great many persons, and from the product of this labor can realize new profits; for example, by selling at a profit the objects he will have had manufactured.

Certain societies have tried to remedy this state of affairs and effect a fairer distribution of wealth by severely limiting either the possession of money or the use that may be made of it. It is especially forbidden to buy another man's labor in order to resell its products. It is society itself that reserves the right to buy a man's labor, paying him the price it decrees as fair. It is also society that takes the initiative with regard to production and commerce. In other words, the political powers assume the direction of all business, including that which elsewhere derives, at least in part, from the spontaneous arrangement.

This method does not seem to have produced, up to the present, excellent results. It certainly diminishes the disorder of production and suppresses useless activities. But it replaces them by others which consist in directing and controlling the phases of actual labor and those of the distribution of products. On the other hand, in this system, labor itself appears less intense and less fruitful than when it is animated by the search for an individual profit. On the whole, the regime thus created has taken root only in nations traditionally accustomed to servitude.

Inequality of condition could not have lasted so long in societies except that it does not encounter an opposition in human nature as intense as one might suppose. It corresponds, indeed, to more or less conscious needs: first of all, that of finding in the spectacle of life at least a minimum of diversity; in the second place, each man, for at least a certain time, can hope that one day or another inequality may favor him by a combination of merit and luck. This prospect introduces an element of interest into life. A society in which equality of conditions was rigorously guaranteed and maintained would fall a prey to somnolence. Yet one sees the same nations, at the same periods, attempt to diminish by law the existing inequalities and hasten to create others, more arbitrary than any in their principle, by means of *sweepstakes* and *lotteries*.

If men readily resign themselves to inequality, they resign themselves even more easily, without exception, to *servitude*. This servitude often accompanies *idolatry* with regard to a person. In the still recent past, the best human minds considered that the crude forms of servitude and idolatry were linked to the primitive state of society, and that the advanced peoples were henceforth incapable of them. Recent years have proved the contrary. With regard to idolatry especially, no nation manages to do without it entirely. When it ceases to be addressed to the men who hold power, it turns toward the individuals, men and women, who have made themselves remarkable in a certain order of actions. The cruder this order of actions is, the more intense is the impulse of idolatry and the more people it carries away. For example, in a curious form of combat which takes place before spectators, one man beats another with his fists to the point of causing him to lose consciousness, and if the victor repeats this exploit within a certain period of time with regard to all ad-

⇒ XIX ⇐

THE END OF LIFE ON EARTH?

WE HAVE DISCUSSED THE ROLE PLAYED BY *war*, WHEN WE traced the development of the human network. We have noted that it constituted a natural consequence of the battles in which animals have always engaged, and that nevertheless these animal combats had not yet assumed the character of war proper.

In all ages, war has caused great sufferings and great destruction. In the past, it has contributed to a certain extent to the predominance of those races most endowed with energy, knowledge, and discipline, and to the extension, tightening, and partial unification of the human network. But it has long since constituted upon earth an anachronistic scourge, and one far from finding its compensation in itself.

Two changes in particular have aggravated war. First, having traditionally been waged by a restricted class of individuals, known as *warriors* or *soldiers*, it has become the enterprise of the *nation* as a whole. Society's entire activity is subordinated to it for as long as it lasts. All the resources of the collectivity are hurled into it. The number of its victims and the extent of its ravages are thereby increased. The goal approached, from one war to the next, is the total destruction of vanquished by victor.

Second, the rapid advances of science and industry that war inspires have put at its disposal increasingly powerful means of destruction. These means have become so great in the recent epoch that they suffice, as we have indicated, to cause life to disappear from the greater part of the earth's surface.

One last new factor, linked to the preceding ones, is that modern war tends to affect the totality of the human network. In other words, it becomes total in a double sense: because it engages the totality of each nation, and because it increasingly engages all nations. The human network is abruptly divided into two camps that seek to destroy each other. For the first time, they have the possibility of doing so. And in the present state of affairs, it is difficult to see what will keep them from doing so sooner or later. We may recall that this mutual destruction risks extending beyond the human network to efface all traces of life on Earth and to sterilize the planet definitively.

If we leave aside these extreme eventualities, the human network finds itself threatened by its own development. Certain parts of the network have in fact acquired a density which appears scarcely compatible with a normal life. Already the products of the soil no longer suffice for the alimentation of the multitudes which continue to increase. And since medicine has recently diminished the frequency and harmfulness of the diseases which even lately tended to compensate for the too-rapid growth of these multitudes, men are obliged to anticipate in short order a state of famine affecting entire populations, whence may emerge the worst disorders.

On the other hand, we have noted in an earlier chapter that the meritorious and almost miraculous effect of diverting into pacific channels recent or future discoveries relating to the energy contained in the material elements would not prevent a more or less imminent destruction of the human network (not to mention other forms of life). It would at best merely postpone and retard its accomplishment.

Two reflections are in order: the first is that the progress of knowledge, and of the powers it bestows over natural forces, becomes, after a certain point, incompatible with a type of existence such as that which the human network affords. This knowledge and this power might accumulate on Earth without excessive danger only if they remained under the control of an extremely powerful and prudent authority animated with intentions above suspicion. But once they circulate more or less freely, they manage to constitute, one day or another, a mortal danger.

The second reflection is that the material growth of the human network, in extent and density, could continue spontaneously, although with great risks of disorder and of futile conflicts, only within certain limits. Beyond these limits, growth is no longer conceivable save if it is subject to a central regulation; as has occurred in the case of the animal organisms, which have been able to subsist only by submitting to this regulation, of which they found the principle and the means within themselves.

Some attempts at planetary organization and central regulation appear in humanity in the last third of a century. But hitherto they have lacked effectiveness. They give the impression that humanity, aware of the danger that threatens it

CONCLUSION

THE PRESENT REPORT CORRESPONDS TO A PARTICULAR AND perhaps extremely transitory situation of the planet which is its object. In other periods, some quite recent, this planet presented an ensemble of characteristics which had every likelihood of remaining virtually the same for hundreds or even thousands of years. Today, we observe a confluence of conditions whose instability is extreme. It is quite likely that the present report will shortly become inaccurate.

In its present state, the Earth, by the existence of man and his works, occupies an extremely advanced position. It has gone farther in certain directions than other cosmic entities where beings apparently more richly endowed have developed. But the way it has taken unfortunately requires, if it is to avert a catastrophic conclusion, those virtues of collective organization with which humanity has always appeared to be ill provided.

111